THE NEW MATHEMATICS

Books by Irving Adler

THE NEW MATHEMATICS

WHAT WE WANT OF OUR SCHOOLS

THE TOOLS OF SCIENCE:
  FROM YARDSTICK TO CYCLOTRON

THE SUN AND ITS FAMILY

MAN-MADE MOONS

MONKEY BUSINESS:
  HOAXES IN THE NAME OF SCIENCE

HOW LIFE BEGAN

MAGIC HOUSE OF NUMBERS

THE STARS: STEPPINGSTONES INTO SPACE

TOOLS IN YOUR LIFE

FIRE IN YOUR LIFE

TIME IN YOUR LIFE

THE SECRET OF LIGHT

IRVING ADLER

THE NEW
MATHEMATICS

With diagrams by Ruth Adler

The John Day Company
New York

© 1958 by Irving and Ruth Adler

Third Impression

QA
93
A3

Contents

Foreword

AS WE go about our daily business, we make frequent use of whole numbers, like 1, 2, 3, and 4, which arise when we count collections of objects. We also use fractions, like ½ and ¼, which arise when measurements are made. These are obviously two different kinds of number, because fractions can never arise as a result of counting alone. In what sense then, do they both deserve to be called numbers? When we say that the fraction 4/2 is equal to the whole number 2, what does this mean? How can a number of one kind be equal to a number of a totally different kind?

These are among the questions which modern mathematics has explored, and for which it has found answers. Here are others:

We sometimes have occasion to use a number like the square-root of two. It seems like a very elusive number that is reluctant to show its face. Either it hides shyly behind a symbol like $\sqrt{2}$, or it reveals itself only piecemeal as a decimal, 1.4, 1.41, 1.414, in a process that never ends. Why doesn't it behave itself and settle down like a decent ordinary fraction with a definite numerator and denominator that can determine its value once and for all?

In elementary algebra we were introduced to negative numbers, and taught such mysterious rules as that the product of two negative numbers is a positive number. Where does such a rule come from?

The electrical engineer uses the number $\sqrt{-1}$ in the equations that describe the behavior of an alternating current. This number is called "imaginary," yet there is nothing imaginary about the electrical current it helps to describe. It is a genuine number, mathematicians assure us, although it is not real. What is the meaning of this paradox?

These are some of the questions that we shall look into in the course of this book as we take a close look at the numbers of everyday life. We shall find the answers in the fact that our number system has not been static, but has been growing, while our conception of what constitutes a number has changed. As we trace this growth, we shall discover the familiar roots of the unfamiliar concepts and terms of modern mathematics.

For mathematics, one of the oldest of the sciences, is growing with the vigor and vitality of youth. It is constantly expanding into new areas of investigation, and works with new concepts that are the fruit of a century-old revolution in mathematical thinking. Associated with the new ideas is a new vocabulary that gives modern mathematical writing its characteristic flavor. To the mathematician, the new ideas expressed by the new words serve as a bright light that penetrates to the core of a problem and helps him see and understand. To the layman, the new vocabulary is often an opaque screen behind which things are going on that he feels he cannot hope to understand. The purpose of this book is to remove that screen, by introducing the reader to the meaning of some of the basic ideas of modern mathematics.

This book is addressed to the average reader who is curious about the new developments in mathematics. It is not a refresher course in high school mathematics. It is not a rehash of old ideas, but an introduction to new ideas, traditionally presented only to the specialist, in advanced mathematics courses on the college senior or graduate level. But, although the ideas are advanced, the presentation is elementary. Anybody who has had high school algebra and geometry will be able to understand and enjoy this book.

A typical text in advanced mathematics today bristles

with such terms as group, ring, field, homomorphism, iso-morphism, and homeomorphism. These unfamiliar looking words make it seem as though mathematics has abandoned its old subject matter, and is no longer concerned with the study of numbers and space. This, of course, is not true. Numbers and space are still very much at the heart of mathematics. The new ideas and terms have arisen in con-nection with a more penetrating analysis of their properties.

Underlying the terms group, ring, and field, for exam-ple, are the old, familiar, simple operations of addition, sub-traction, multiplication, and division. The mathematician has discovered that these operations are not the exclusive property of numbers alone. So he studies them in their most general form, in order to discover rules that will be valid in any context in which the operations are performed.

The outlook of the modern mathematician is indicated in his frequent use of the word stem "morph," meaning form, as in the words homomorphism, isomorphism, and homeomorphism. The mathematician sees the number sys-tem as a complex of interrelated *structures*. He studies these structures separately, and in their relationships to each other. The exploration of these structures has revealed that we have, not *a* number system, but number systems; not algebra, but algebras; not geometry, but geometries; not space, but spaces. While the properties of numbers and space have been generalized, the subject matter of mathe-matics has been pluralized.

The central thread around which the book is organized is the expansion of the number system, from natural num-bers to integers to rational numbers to real numbers to complex numbers. Although this sequence of steps in the development of the number system parallels very roughly historical stages in the development of the concept of num-ber, the organization of the book is not chronological or historical. It is a logical organization from the modern point of view, showing how the various number systems are re-lated to each other. The development outlined here might be referred to as "operation bootstrap." The system of natural numbers (the whole numbers used for counting) has defects that limit its usefulness. The story presented here shows how mathematics has lifted itself by its own bootstraps, using the defective system of natural numbers to construct bigger and better number systems that eliminate the defects.

At each stage of the construction of the expanded number systems, we encounter some of the structures such as groups, rings and fields that receive so much attention in modern mathematics. These modern concepts are introduced first by means of familiar examples in the number systems, and then other less familiar examples are given, too. As he reads the sections devoted to these modern concepts, the reader will be aware of the fact that he is merely nibbling at the corner of a great rug that has a beautiful but intricate design woven into it. If what he sees from the corner arouses his curiosity about the main design, it is hoped that he will satisfy this curiosity by systematic study from some of the standard text-books. A bibliography is given at the end of the book.

To get the most value and enjoyment out of this book, read it with pencil and paper in hand. Verify the steps of each argument, work through all examples given, and do other examples like them. A "Do It Yourself" section at the end of each chapter gives you an opportunity to strengthen through use your understanding of the new ideas you will acquire in the book.

THE NEW MATHEMATICS

CHAPTER I

Numbers for Counting

WE ARE thoroughly familiar with the faces of the people with whom we live. Yet we are rarely conscious of the details of their features. If, as we look at a familiar face, we do take particular notice of the details, such as a curve of the lip, or a line in the forehead, it seems as though we are seeing them for the first time. Then, seeing these features that we never notice, we suddenly have the feeling that we are looking at the face of a stranger. We shall have a similar experience with the familiar numbers of everyday life. When we use these numbers, we take advantage of certain properties that they have. However, we are so accustomed to these properties that we are hardly aware of them as we use them. We shall now take particular notice of these properties, and list them explicitly. Looking at the familiar features of ordinary numbers, we shall see the strange new face of modern mathematics.

The first numbers we all learn to use are those we need to answer the question, "How many?" They are the numbers 1, 2, 3, 4, 5, and so on. There is an endless chain of these numbers. We use them for counting, and we perform calculations with them, such as addition and multiplication. Let us take a close look at these simple acts.

Counting

Suppose that on Tuesday evening you want to see how many days are left till the end of the week. It is likely that you will take count in this way: You will call off the names of the days, Wednesday, Thursday, Friday, and Saturday, and, for each day that you name, you will turn down one finger on your right hand. After completing the list of days, you find that you have turned down all the fingers on your right hand except the thumb. So you conclude that there are *four* days left till the end of the week. We find hidden in this procedure three important mathematical concepts: the idea of a *mapping*, the idea of a *one-to-one correspondence*, and the idea of *cardinal number*.

A mapping is a matching operation between two sets of objects: to each member of one set a member of the other set is assigned as partner. The two sets in this case are the set of days being counted, and the set of fingers on your hand. You set up a mapping when you single out a finger to turn down for each day you count. The mapping might be summarized in the following table:

Wednesday → little finger
Thursday → ring finger
Friday   → middle finger
Saturday → index finger

The arrowheads indicate that the mapping has a direction. You select a finger for each day you name. This is not the same as selecting a day for each finger. To specify the direction of the mapping, we say that it is a mapping of the set of days named *into* the set of fingers. We refer to the finger into which a day is mapped as its *image* under the mapping.

Another mapping is shown in the diagram below. In this mapping, a set of names of people has been mapped into the set of whole numbers from 20 to 24 by assigning to each name the person's age in years:

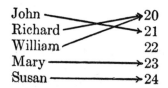

This mapping differs from the other one in one important respect. The two names, Richard and William, are both

14

mapped into the same number. This is an example of a *many-to-one mapping,* in which a single object may be the image of more than one object. In the mapping of days into fingers, however, no two days were mapped into the same finger. This is an example of a *one-to-one mapping,* in which each object is the image of at most one object.

In the mapping of the set of days into the fingers of the right hand, one of the fingers, the thumb, wasn't used at all. For this reason the mapping of the set of days into the set of fingers on the right hand is not reversible. If we try to reverse it, we find that there is no mapping of the thumb into a day. We do not consider it a mapping then, because a mapping should provide an image for each object in the set on which the mapping is performed. However, if we consider *only the set of fingers turned down,* then the mapping is reversible. Then, while each day named has a separate finger as its image, in the reverse mapping, each finger has a separate day as its image. In this case we say that the two sets are in *one-to-one correspondence.* Two sets are in one-to-one correspondence when there is a reversible mapping that assigns each member of one set to one and only one partner in the other. The diagram below, using double-headed arrows, shows the one-to-one correspondence between the set of days and the set of fingers turned down:

Wednesday ⟷ little finger
Thursday ⟷ ring finger
Friday   ⟷ middle finger
Saturday ⟷ index finger

When two sets can be put into one-to-one correspondence by some mapping, we say that they contain the same number of objects, or have the same *cardinal number.* All sets that have the same cardinal number can be put into one-to-one correspondence with each other. They form a family of sets associated with that cardinal number. Each cardinal number has its own family of sets. For example, sets consisting of *single objects only* belong to the family of sets associated with the number we call *one.* Sets of *pairs of*

15

objects belong to the family of sets associated with the number we call *two*. Sets of triples belong to the family of sets associated with the number we call *three,* and so on.

Any set we ever deal with belongs to one of these families. When we ask the question, "How many objects are there in the set?", it is really like asking, "Which family of sets does it belong to?" To answer the question, we follow this procedure: We pick one set from each family, and use it as a standard set for making comparisons. We match the set we are interested in against these standard sets, until we find one with which it can be put into one-to-one correspondence. In this way we identify the family of sets that it belongs to, and the cardinal number associated with that family. This is precisely what you do when you match days against fingers. You use the set consisting of your little finger alone as a standard set to represent the number *one*. You use the set consisting of little finger and ring finger as a standard set to represent the number *two*. You use the set consisting of little finger, ring finger, and middle finger as a standard set to represent the number *three*. The set consisting of little finger, ring finger, middle finger, and index finger is your standard set representing the number *four*. That is why you drew the conclusion, in this case, that there are four more days to the end of the week.

On other occasions, we use a method of counting that is more sophisticated but is essentially the same. We count out four objects by saying to ourselves, "one, two, three, four." As we count, we set up a one-to-one correspondence between the objects we are counting and sets of spoken number-names. The first object is matched with the set consisting of the single word, "one." The first two are matched with the set consisting of the words, "one, two." The first three are matched with the set consisting of the words, "one, two, three." And so on. By using the number names of the numbers in order of size, we keep enlarging the standard set step by step. When the count ends, we know that the last number-name used is the cardinal number of

16

the last standard set against which we matched the objects we are counting. So it is also the cardinal number of the counted objects. By using standard sets made up of number names arranged in order we telescope a whole series of matching operations into one, and end up with the answer to the question, "How many?"

Addition

A typical problem in addition is to find the sum of the numbers 2 and 3. The meaning of this problem can be restated in terms of sets of objects in this way: Suppose you have one set of objects whose cardinal number is 2, and another set of objects, different from those in the first set, and whose cardinal number is 3. A larger set is formed when these two sets are united. What is the cardinal number of the united set?

We can answer this question by actually forming such a united set, and then identifying the standard set with which it can be put into one-to-one correspondence. This is the procedure of the beginner in arithmetic, who first turns down two fingers, then turns down three more fingers, and finally matches the set of turned down fingers against the standard set consisting of the spoken words, "one, two, three, four, five." However, experienced calculators use a short-cut for getting the answer. Having carried out the process of uniting and counting sets of objects many times before, we record the results in an *addition table* which we memorize. Then, any time we want to find the sum of two numbers, we don't have to manipulate sets of objects again. We merely consult the table.

Using the addition table instead of adding on our fingers is more than just a time-saving convenience. It is an act of abstraction that *has changed the meaning of addition.* When we add on our fingers, we are actually working with cardinal numbers, which are properties of sets of objects. When we use the addition table, we are performing an operation on abstract symbols. This operation can now be performed

17

without regard to what the symbols stood for in the first place. Let us examine this abstract operation a little more closely.

We have a set of symbols, 1, 2, 3, 4, and so on, that we call numbers. If we pick any one of them, and then pick another one, the addition table assigns to this pair of numbers another number called its sum. For example, if we pick the number 2 first, and the number 3 next, the table assigns as their sum the number 5. We have picked the pair of numbers 2 and 3 in a definite order, specifying that the two is first and the 3 is second. So we can refer to it as the ordered pair (2, 3). What the addition table does is assign a definite number called the sum to every ordered pair of numbers. When we describe it in this way, we recognize that *addition is a mapping*. It maps the set of ordered pairs of numbers into the set of single numbers. We usually show the mapping in a series of statements like this: $2 + 3 = 5$, $2 + 4 = 6$, $2 + 5 = 7$, etc. Its nature as a mapping shows up more clearly if we write it this way:

$$(2, 3) \xrightarrow{\;+\;} 5$$

$$(2, 4) \xrightarrow{\;+\;} 6$$

$$(2, 5) \xrightarrow{\;+\;} 7$$

etc.

The plus sign printed over the arrows is a reminder that the mapping shown is the special mapping called addition. It is only one of a multitude of possible mappings. We could, if we wished, set up a mapping of pairs of numbers into the letters of the alphabet. If we wished, we could map pairs of numbers into people's names. We have a wide choice of mappings, because we can map any set of objects into any other set of objects in any way we please. The plus sign symbolizing addition calls our attention to the fact that it is a very special mapping with special characteristics. Now let us examine some of these characteristics.

18

We observe, first, that the numbers we are pairing off in our ordered pairs are selected from the list of symbols, 1, 2, 3, 4, etc. To distinguish this set of symbols from the cardinal numbers from which they were derived, let us give it a name. We shall call it the system of *natural numbers*. We observe next that the number assigned as sum to each ordered pair is selected *from the same set*, the system of natural numbers. A mapping which assigns to each ordered pair of objects in a set another object selected from the same set is called a *binary operation*. So addition is an example of a binary operation defined on the system of natural numbers.

If we consult the addition table, we find that $1 + 4 = 5$, $2 + 3 = 5$, $3 + 2 = 5$, and $4 + 1 = 5$. The different ordered pairs, (1, 4), (2, 3), (3, 2), and (4, 1) are all mapped into the same image, 5. So addition is a many-to-one mapping. In particular, an ordered pair like (2, 3) and the pair (3, 2), obtained by having the 2 and 3 change places, both have the same image. We could write $2 + 3 = 3 + 2$. A similar statement is true for the sum of every ordered pair of natural numbers. We find that $5 + 2 = 2 + 5$, $9 + 16 = 16 + 9$, etc. This characteristic of the addition of natural numbers can be summarized in the following rule: If the letter a stands for any natural number, and the letter b stands for any natural number, then $a + b = b + a$. That is, if the natural numbers being added *commute* or change places, the sum is still the same. So this rule is known as the *commutative law of addition,* and we say that addition of natural numbers is a commutative operation.

We are so accustomed to using the commutative law of addition that it may seem to be obvious, and hardly worth mentioning. But it needs special mention because, while some binary operations, like addition of natural numbers, obey a commutative law, there are others that do not. For example, one of the operations we learned in elementary school arithmetic is called *division*, and is denoted by the symbol $\div$. It is not a commutative operation, because the numbers being divided cannot, in general, change places without changing the result. For example, $8 \div 2$ is not equal to $2 \div 8$.

Addition, as we have talked about it so far, is an operation performed on a *pair* of numbers. We can also extend it to three numbers. We can add three numbers by first adding two of them, and then adding the sum to the third. However, for three numbers like 2, 3, and 7, listed in a definite order, we have a choice of two ways of doing it. We might add the sum of 2 and 3 to 7, or we might add 2 to the sum of 3 and 7. These two possibilities can be written down in this form: $(2 + 3) + 7$, and $2 + (3 + 7)$. In this notation, the parentheses indicate which sum is to be found first. When we carry out these additions, we find that it doesn't make any difference which sum is found first, because the results come out the same: $(2 + 3) + 7 = 5 + 7 = 12$, and $2 + (3 + 7) = 2 + 10 = 12$. This is a characteristic of the addition of three natural numbers, no matter what numbers are used. It is expressed in the rule, $(a + b) + c = a + (b + c)$, where a, b, and c stand for any natural numbers. This rule says that in the first step of the addition we are free to associate the middle number either with the number on the left or with the number on the right. So the rule is known as the *associative law of addition*, and we say that addition of natural numbers is an associative operation. Since it makes no difference which pair of numbers we add first, we may as well leave out the parentheses altogether, and write the sum of a, b, and c as $a + b + c$, where it is understood that $a + b + c = a + (b + c) = (a + b) + c$.

The associative law, too, deserves special mention because it is a special property of addition of natural numbers, which it shares with some binary operations but not with all. For example, suppose we use the symbol av to designate the operation "take the average of." It is a binary operation that can be performed on the familiar whole numbers and fractions that we use every day. In this notation, $8 \; av \; 16$ means the average of 8 and 16, which is 12. The symbol 12 *av* 12 means the average of 12 and 12, which is also 12. The symbol 16 *av* 12 means 14, and the symbol 8 *av* 14 means 11. This operation does not obey an associative law, because (8 *av* 16) *av* 12 is *not* equal to 8 *av* (16 *av* 12). In fact, (8 *av* 16) *av* 12 means 12 *av* 12, or 12, while 8 *av* (16 *av* 12) means 8 *av* 14, or 11.

By a step-by-step process, the use of the commutative law and the associative law for addition of natural numbers can be extended into a general rule for the sum of any finite selection of natural numbers: When you add a finite selection of natural numbers, you can list them in any order, and group them as you please. The sum will always come out the same.

Multiplication

The meaning of multiplication of natural numbers, like the meaning of addition, can be stated first in terms of sets of objects. To multiply 2 times 3, we set up a rectangular array of objects, consisting of two rows, with three objects in each row. Then we find the cardinal number of

this set. In general, to multiply the numbers a and b, we find the cardinal number of a set consisting of a rows with b objects in each row. The answer is called the product of a and b, and is designated by $a \cdot b$, where we use a dot as the symbol for multiplication. Once we have found the product of two natural numbers, we can record it for future reference in a multiplication table. Then we can separate the operation of multiplication from its original meaning of finding the cardinal number of a rectangular array of objects. We can think of it instead as merely a mapping of ordered pairs of natural numbers into the system of natural numbers. We usually show the mapping by a series of statements like this: $2 \cdot 3 = 6$, $2 \cdot 4 = 8$, $2 \cdot 5 = 10$, etc.

21

However, as in the case of addition, we can express it with the help of arrows:

$$(2, 3) \xrightarrow{\cdot} 6$$

$$(2, 4) \xrightarrow{\cdot} 8$$

$$(2, 5) \xrightarrow{\cdot} 10$$
etc.

Since the mapping is defined for every ordered pair of natural numbers, and the image under the mapping is always a natural number, multiplication, like addition, is a binary operation on the system of natural numbers. We know from our experience with multiplication of natural numbers that $2 \cdot 3 = 3 \cdot 2$, $2 \cdot 4 = 4 \cdot 2$, $2 \cdot 5 = 5 \cdot 2$, etc. In general, if a and b are any natural numbers, $a \cdot b = b \cdot a$. This is known as the *commutative law of multiplication*. Multiplication, like addition, also obeys an *associative law*: $a \cdot (b \cdot c) = (a \cdot b) \cdot c$. This is seen, for example, in the fact that $2 \cdot (3 \cdot 5) = 2 \cdot 15 = 30$, and $(2 \cdot 3) \cdot 5 = 6 \cdot 5 = 30$. Because of this law, we can write the product of three numbers without parentheses, and give it a definite meaning: $a \cdot b \cdot c = a \cdot (b \cdot c) = (a \cdot b) \cdot c$. Combining the commutative law and associative law of multiplication leads to the general rule: when you multiply a finite selection of natural numbers, you can list them in any order, and group them as you please. The product will always come out the same.

There is one more characteristic of the multiplication of natural numbers that links it with addition. We can understand it best by going back to the original meaning of multiplication as finding the cardinal number of a rectangular array, and the original meaning of addition as finding the cardinal number of a united set. Printed below is a rectangular array of stars, consisting of three rows with nine stars in each row. The number of stars in this rectangular array is $3 \cdot 9$. Since a row of nine stars can be thought of as the first five stars united with four other stars, we can write $9 = 5 + 4$. So the number of stars in the rectangular array can also be written as $3 \cdot (5 + 4)$. Now, suppose we move the first five stars in each row over to the left, so that a space separates them from the rest of the stars in the same row. The effect is to split our rectangle into two rectangles. One rectangle has three rows with five stars in each row, so it contains $3 \cdot 5$ stars. The other rectangle has three rows with four stars in each row, so it contains $3 \cdot 4$ stars. Since we get the original rectangle by uniting the two smaller rectangles, the number of stars in the original rectangle is the sum of the numbers of stars in the two smaller rectangles. This fact is expressed in the statement that $3 \cdot (5 + 4) = (3 \cdot 5) + (3 \cdot 4)$. We can verify the cor-

rectness of the statement by noting that $3 \cdot 9 = 27$, and $15 + 12 = 27$. In general, if a, b, and c, stand for natural numbers, $a \cdot (b + c) = (a \cdot b) + (a \cdot c)$. Similarly, $(b + c) \cdot a = (b \cdot a) + (c \cdot a)$. This rule is known as the *distributive law* and expresses the fact that multiplication is distributive with respect to addition. That is, the multiplier can be distributed among the individual terms in the expression it multiplies. In the statement of this law, multiplication and addition cannot change places. While $3 + (5 \cdot 4) = 3 + 20 = 23$, $(3 + 5) \cdot (3 + 4) = 8 \cdot 7 = 56$, so that addition is *not* distributive with respect to multiplication. It is customary, in writing an expression like $(a \cdot b) + (a \cdot c)$ to leave the parentheses out, so that it looks like this: $a \cdot b + a \cdot c$. In such an expression, which gives instructions for doing both multiplication and addition of some numbers, it is understood that the multiplications must be done first.

The Five Laws

We originally introduced the natural numbers as symbols for the cardinal numbers. Then we made these observations about them: There are two binary operations defined on the natural number system, and we call them addition and multiplication. The properties of these operations are embodied in the addition and multiplication tables. By examining these tables, we found five laws that are obeyed by the natural number system: the commutative and associative laws of addition, the commutative and associative laws of multiplication, and the distributive law which asserts that multiplication is distributive with respect to addition. These laws have a special significance in the development of our notion of what a number is. We find that when we carry out computations with numbers we do not have to keep in mind their original meaning as cardinal numbers. It is enough to think of them as abstract symbols related to each other by addition and multiplication tables that obey these five laws. This fact suggests that we redefine numbers as follows: *A number system is any collection of objects on which two binary operations called addition and multiplication are defined, such that addition is commutative and associative, multiplication is commutative and associative, and multiplication is distributive with respect to addition.*

This definition is a declaration of independence for the idea of a number system. It frees it from its cardinal-number ancestry and permits it to lead its own life. It allows it to expand and grow. When a number system is defined in this way, we find that there is not just one number system, but many number systems. We find, too, that it is possible for one number system to be part of a larger number system, which in turn is part of a still larger number system, and so on. In fact, the core of this book is the systematic construction of larger and larger number systems, using the natural numbers as a foundation. At each stage of the construction we shall recognize that we have built a number system when we find that it has two binary operations that obey the five laws:

I. $a + b = b + a$

II. $(a + b) + c = a + (b + c)$

III. $a \cdot b = b \cdot a$

IV. $(a \cdot b) \cdot c = a \cdot (b \cdot c)$

V. $a \cdot (b + c) = a \cdot b + a \cdot c$

or $(b + c) \cdot a = b \cdot a + c \cdot a$

Large and Small Numbers

The natural number system has some other important characteristics besides the five laws. One of these is that we can compare any two numbers in it for size. The number 5 is larger than 4, and 4 in turn is larger than 3. The notion of larger and smaller is derived from addition in this way: We say that b is larger than a if b is equal to the sum of a and some other natural number. For example, 5 is larger than 4, because $5 = 4 + 1$; 5 is larger than 3, because $5 = 3 + 2$.

One System with Many Disguises

There are many different ways of writing the natural numbers. In the system of Arabic numerals that we use every day, the numbers one, two, three, four and five are written as 1, 2, 3, 4, 5. In Roman numerals, still used on clock faces and monuments, they are written as I, II, III, IV, V. In Hebrew they are written as the first five letters of the alphabet. If we think of these different systems of numerals as symbols for the cardinal numbers, then they are different ways of representing one and the same number system. However, we may also think of each system of numerals as a separate number system in its own right, with addition and multiplication defined by its addition and multiplication tables. The Arabic, the Roman, and the Hebrew numerals could then be referred to legitimately as three separate number systems. But they are number systems that can be used interchangeably, so, although they are separate systems, they are still somehow the same. In the next chapter we shall encounter number systems that are not interchangeable and may not be considered the same. In order to recognize when number systems are interchangeable, and when they are not, we have to define what we mean when we say different systems are the same.

What we have in mind is that they have the *same structure.* For two number systems to have the same structure, each number in one system must have a counterpart in the other system. We can express this requirement in technical language by saying that there must be a mapping of one system into the other that places them in one-to-one correspondence. But the one-to-one correspondence alone is not enough. We want to be sure, too, that the results of computations in one system will correspond to the results of computations in the other system. So we say that two number systems have the same structure, or are *isomorphic,* if (1) there is a mapping of one into the other that puts them into one-to-one correspondence, and (2) under this mapping, sums and products are preserved. The requirement can also be stated in this way: Under the mapping, each element in one system has an image in the other. Moreover, the image of the sum of two numbers is the sum of the images; and the image of the product is the product of the images. Comparing Arabic numerals and Roman numerals, for example, we can set up a one-to-one correspondence, shown in part in this table:

$$1 \longleftrightarrow \text{I}$$
$$2 \longleftrightarrow \text{II}$$
$$3 \longleftrightarrow \text{III}$$
$$4 \longleftrightarrow \text{IV}$$
$$5 \longleftrightarrow \text{V}$$
$$6 \longleftrightarrow \text{VI}$$

Each system has its own addition and multiplication tables, part of which is shown in the customary square arrangements below:

+	1	2	3
1	2	3	4
2	3	4	5
3	4	5	6

+	I	II	III
I	II	III	IV
II	III	IV	V
III	IV	V	VI

Addition

26

	·	1	2	3
	1	1	2	3
Multiplication	2	2	4	6
	3	3	6	9

·	I	II	III
I	I	II	III
II	II	IV	VI
III	III	VI	IX

Under the mapping the image of 2 is II, and the image of 3 is III. The sum of 2 and 3 is 5. The sum of II and III is V, which is the image of 5. So the sum of the images is the image of the sum. The product of 2 and 3 is 6. The product of II and III is VI, which is the image of 6. So the product of the images is the image of the product. Arabic numerals and Roman numerals, considered as separate number systems, are isomorphic to each other. Although numbers in one system look different from numbers in the other system, the relationships within the systems, as expressed in the addition and multiplication tables, have the same structure. So the two systems are really only one structure appearing in two different styles of dress.

Zero and One

Arabic numerals displaced all others because of their great convenience. They are most convenient to use because they give us a way of writing an indefinite amount of numbers while using only a small number of symbols called *digits*. This feat is accomplished by attaching different meanings to the same digit. In the number 111, three one's are used, and each has a different meaning. The 1 on the extreme right stands for the number *one*. The 1 in the second column from the right stands for the number *ten,* and the 1 in the third column stands for the number *one hundred*. The symbol stands for the sum of one, ten, and one hundred. Because the meaning of a digit depends on its position in the written numeral, we say the Arabic system of numerals is a *place value* system. To represent three *hundreds* plus two *tens* plus five *ones,* we write 325.

Now suppose we want to write the symbol for three *tens*. We put a 3 into the second column from the left. But we won't recognize it as the second column unless we write something down in the first column. This makes it necessary to think of three tens as three tens plus *no ones*, and to introduce a symbol to represent the absence of ones. We use the symbol 0 for this purpose, and call it zero. The concept of a number representing *none* was first conceived by the Hindus, and was later taken over by the Arabs and built into their system of numerals. Zero became a new number in the natural number system, and had to be incorporated into the addition and multiplication tables in a way which is consistent with the rest of the tables. This was done by using these rules for computation with zero: zero plus any number gives that number again; and zero times any number gives zero. The first of these rules can be written in symbols as follows: $0 + x = x$, for any natural number x. In later chapters, we shall be building up some other number systems. It will be necessary for us to find out whether these number systems contain an element that behaves like the zero of the natural number system. In our search for a zero element, we shall use the first rule as our criterion. If a number system contains a number a such that $a + x = x$, for all numbers x in that system, then we shall call a a *zero element*.

The distinguishing feature of a zero element is that *adding* it to another number leaves that number unchanged. There is a natural number that has the same relationship to multiplication that zero has to addition. This number is the number *one*, which obeys the rule: $1 \cdot x = x$, for all natural numbers x. That is, *multiplying* a number by 1 leaves that number unchanged. In the number systems we explore later, we shall sometimes find an element that has this property, and shall call it a *unity element*.

When we write out sums, we always use the symbol $+$ to stand for the operation of addition. We could, if we wished, use some other symbol instead, as long as we agreed on its meaning. We might, for example, use the symbol * to represent the operation. In that case, the characteristic property of 0 could be written in this way: $0 * x = x$. In the same way, we could, if we wished, change the symbol for multiplication. If, temporarily, we used the symbol $*$ to represent multiplication, then the characteristic property of 1 would be written as follows: $1 * x = x$.

The similarity in form of these two statements emphasizes the fact that 0 and 1 really both have the same property, except that each has it in relation to another operation. They are both examples of what is known as an *identity* element. In any system in which a binary operation is defined, and is symbolized by $*$, if there is an element e that has the property $e * x = x$, for all values x in the system, then e is called an identity element. The letter e is used in this definition of an identity element because it is the initial letter of the German word *einheit,* which means *unity.*

Now we can state more precisely how the terms *zero element* and *unity element* are used in mathematics today. Whenever a binary operation is denoted by the symbol $+$ and is called "plus," the identity element for that operation is called a *zero element,* and is denoted by 0. Whenever a binary operation is denoted by the symbol $\cdot$, and is called "times," the identity element for that operation is called a *unity element* and is denoted by 1. We shall use this convention many times in later chapters.

Points on a Line

It is possible to represent the natural numbers as points on a line. On any straight line, choose a point and call it 0. This point divides the line into two half-lines. On one of these half-lines, choose another point and call it 1. Now continue locating points further and further away from 0 by making the distance from each point to the next one the same length as the distance from 0 to 1. Label these new points successively 2, 3, 4, 5, etc. We then have an endless sequence of points that is in one-to-one correspondence with the natural number system. The number attached to each point is its distance from 0, expressed in terms of the distance from 0 to 1 as the unit of length.

We can define addition and multiplication for these points by means of geometric constructions. Here, for example, is one way of doing it: To add a and b, measure out from a, in the direction away from 0, a length equal to the distance from 0 to b. The point located in this way has a distance from 0 equal to $a + b$. To multiply a and b,

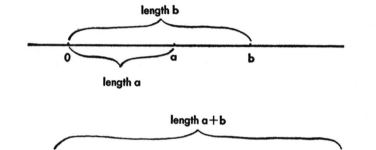

first draw another line intersecting this one at 0. Use the same scheme for assigning numbers to points on this line. Locate points $1'$, $2'$, $3'$, etc., on the line, so that successive points are separated by equal distances, all equal to the distance from 0 to $1'$. Join $1'$ on the new line to a on the original line. Locate b' on the new line at a distance from 0 equal to b. Then through b' draw a line parallel to the line just drawn from $1'$ to a. It will cross the original line at a point that will represent $a \cdot b$.

The construction for addition obviously corresponds to ordinary addition of numbers. The construction for multiplication corresponds to ordinary multiplication for this reason: If we designate by x the point that we have defined

30

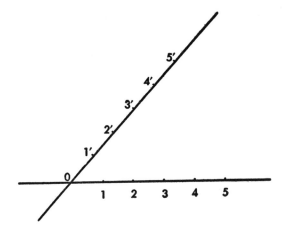

as the product of a and b, then x is its distance from 0. The triangles (0 1' a) and (0 b' x) are similar, so their corresponding sides are proportional. Then $1 : b = a : x$. From this proportion, we find that $x = a \cdot b$. With addition and multiplication defined by these constructions, the system of points on the half-line is isomorphic to the natural number system.

After we have assigned numbers in this way to points on a line, we find that there are still many points on the line that do not have numbers. All of our numbers are on one side of 0. There are none on the other side. Moreover, we

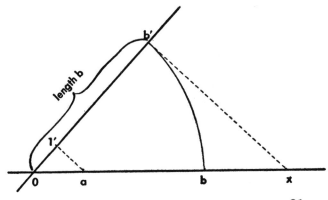

31

have not assigned numbers to the points between those that represent successive natural numbers. For example, there are no numbers assigned to the points that lie between 0 and 1. This is a defect that will be remedied step by step as we go along. One of our chief purposes will be to build up a number system that has enough points in it for us to assign a number for every point on the line. We hope to do it, too, in such a way that the expanded number system and the whole line will be isomorphic.

The Natural Numbers

So far we have encountered several different systems that are capable of representing the natural numbers. One system consists of the common Arabic numerals, with their addition and multiplication tables. A second one consists of the Roman numerals, with their tables. The third system consists of points on a line, and the appropriate constructions for adding or multiplying them. This variety of representations raises the question, "What is the natural number system, anyhow?"

We might try to answer this question by listing some characteristics that all these number systems have in common. All three, for example, obey the five laws. But this is not an adequate answer, because *all* number systems, as we have defined the term, will obey these five laws. And we intend to produce some number systems that are not interchangeable with the natural number system at all. To define the natural number system, we must list not merely characteristics that all of its representations have in common. We must note particularly its *distinguishing* characteristics. This is done by choosing the defining characteristics in such a way that all systems that have these characteristics must be isomorphic to each other. Such a selection of characteristics that effectively defines one and only one structure is called a system of axioms for the structure. Here is a system of axioms for the natural number system (not including 0), first formulated by the mathematician Peano:

32

A set of elements is called a natural number system if it has the following characteristics:

(1) It contains an element called 1.
(2) For every member in the system, there is another member (and only one) called its successor.
(3) Two distinct members do not have the same successor.
(4) There is no member of the system that has 1 as its successor.
(5) If a set of elements belonging to the system contains 1, and, for each member that it contains, also contains its successor, then this set contains the whole system.

Notice that addition and multiplication are not mentioned in these axioms at all. Peano defined these operations in terms of his axioms as follows: For any natural numbers x and y,

let $x + 1 =$ the successor of x;
let $x +$ (the successor of y) = the successor of $(x + y)$;
let $x \cdot 1 = x$;
let $x \cdot$ (the successor of y) = $x \cdot y + x$.

With these definitions it is possible to prove that the natural number system obeys the five laws.

What Peano did for the natural number system is typical of the way in which mathematical structures are studied today. In modern mathematics, a mathematical structure is often defined as a set of objects that satisfies a specified set of axioms. If the structure defined is to be unique, the axioms are chosen so that all systems that satisfy the axioms will be isomorphic to each other. Different sets of axioms have been formulated for the various mathematical structures needed in practical applications.

DO IT YOURSELF

1. By using double-headed arrows, as on page 26, set up a one-to-one correspondence between the numbers 1, 2,

3, 4, 5 and the letters a, e, i, o, u.

2. An addition operation for the system consisting of two elements, a and b, is defined by the following table:

+	a	b
a	a	b
b	b	a

a) Does this system have a zero element?

b) Show that addition is commutative in this system.

c) Verify from the table that $a + (a + b) = (a + a) + b$.

3. Let the symbol M stand for the binary operation, "take the maximum of." For example, $5\ M\ 7$ means 7; $8\ M\ 3$ means 8; $6\ M\ 6$ means 6. Compare $8\ M\ 3$ with $3\ M\ 8$. If a and b are any two natural numbers, compare $a\ M\ b$ with $b\ M\ a$. Is the operation M commutative? Compare $8\ M\ (3\ M\ 7)$ with $(8\ M\ 3)\ M\ 7$. In general, if a, b, and c are any three natural numbers, compare $a\ M\ (b\ M\ c)$ with $(a\ M\ b)\ M\ c$. Is the operation M associative?

CHAPTER II

Number Systems without "Numbers"

THE word "number," as we use it in everyday life, refers to a symbol associated with counting or measuring. We have broken away from this usage in the definition of a number system given in Chapter I. We defined a number system as any set of objects on which two binary operations are defined that obey the five laws listed on pages 24-5. In this definition, there is no reference to counting or measuring. The five laws are concerned only with the way in which the numbers are related to each other by the addition and multiplication tables. To emphasize this fact, we separated the concept of natural number from that of cardinal number. While cardinal numbers are properties of actual sets of objects, and are intrinsically related to counting, natural numbers are abstract symbols whose entire meaning lies in the formal rules by which we manipulate them.

Nevertheless, the natural numbers do not convey the full meaning of our break with common usage in the definition of number. Introducing the natural numbers effected a separation from the cardinal numbers, but not a divorce. The cardinal number system is still lurking in the background, because it is isomorphic to the natural number system. This fact may arouse the suspicion that no significant change in the concept of number has really been introduced, and that numbers are still essentially bound up with counting and measuring. However, a real change *has* been introduced by our definition of number system. The purpose of this chapter is to demonstrate this fact convincingly by producing some number systems without "numbers." These number systems will consist of elements that have no direct relationship to counting or measuring, and so are not "numbers" in the sense in which the word is commonly used. However, they will be genuine number systems in the sense of our definition.

Subsets of a Set

We shall construct these number systems with the help of the simple notion of a set. A *set* is any collection of objects. The objects that belong to a set are called its *elements*. A set is defined by specifying which objects are elements of the set. This may be done by stating some rule by which the elements can be identified, or by actually putting the elements on display. The symbol commonly used for a set is a pair of braces, with the elements of the set on display inside, or with the rule by which they are identified printed inside. For example, here is a set defined by a rule:

{natural numbers larger than 4, but less than 10}

The same set can be represented by putting its elements on display:

{5, 6, 7, 8, 9}

Other sets can be formed from a given set by removing some of its elements. For example, if we remove the elements 5, 7, and 8 from the set shown above, we are left with the set {6, 9}. It is convenient to extend the notion of set to include what is left if we remove *all* the elements. It will be a "set" with no elements in it, and will be referred to as the *empty set*. To symbolize it, we shall show a pair of braces with no elements on display inside. A set obtained by removing none, or some, or all of the elements of a given set is called a *subset* of that set. For example, the set {x, y, z} has eight subsets, listed below:

36

$$\{x, y, z\} \quad \{x, y\} \quad \{x, z\} \quad \{y, z\}$$
$$\{x\} \qquad \{y\} \qquad \{z\} \qquad \{\ \}$$

Notice that the given set is one of its own subsets, and the empty set is one of the subsets, too.

Operations on Subsets

To define a number system, we must first specify what the elements of the number system are. We shall use as elements all the subsets of a given set. As a specific example, let us build a number system out of the subsets of the set $\{x, y, z\}$. For convenience in talking about them, let us assign a name to each of these subsets. We shall use capital letters for their names, as follows:

$$I = \{x, y, z\} \quad D = \{x\}$$
$$A = \{x, y\} \qquad E = \{y\}$$
$$B = \{x, z\} \qquad F = \{z\}$$
$$C = \{y, z\} \qquad 0 = \{\ \}$$

The symbols I and 0 are included among the names used for reasons that will become clear later.

The next step is to define two binary operations on these elements. A binary operation is defined when we set up some rule for assigning to each ordered pair of subsets some particular subset in the same list. We define the operation of forming a *union* of two subsets by means of this rule: The union of two subsets is another subset formed by taking as its elements those elements that are in *one or the other* of the subsets being united. For example, A contains the elements x and y. B contains the elements x and z. The elements that are in one or the other are x, y, and z. So the union of A and B is the set $\{x, y, z\}$, which we have called I. The union operation will be the "addition" operation of this number system. However, we shall not use the plus sign to represent it. Instead, we shall use the symbol $\cup$. The union of A and B will be written as $A \cup B$, and is read as "A union B." We have seen that $A \cup B = I$. The method

37

of finding the union of two subsets will be clear from the following examples:

$$I \cup C = \{x, y, z\} \cup \{y, z\} = \{x, y, z\} = I$$
$$D \cup E = \{x\} \cup \{y\} = \{x, y\} = A$$
$$C \cup 0 = \{y, z\} \cup \{\ \} = \{y, z\} = C$$

The results of forming all possible unions can be summarized in this table of unions (the addition table for the number system we are constructing):

$\cup$	I	A	B	C	D	E	F	0
I	I	I	I	I	I	I	I	I
A	I	A	I	I	A	A	I	A
B	I	I	B	I	B	I	B	B
C	I	I	I	C	I	C	C	C
D	I	A	B	I	D	A	B	D
E	I	A	I	C	A	E	C	E
F	I	I	B	C	B	C	F	F
0	I	A	B	C	D	E	F	0

The second binary operation we define is that of forming the *intersection* of two subsets. The intersection of two subsets is another subset formed by taking as its elements all those elements that are *in both* of the subsets being intersected. For example, A contains the elements x and y. B contains the elements x and z. Only the element x is in both A and B. So the intersection of A and B is the subset $\{x\}$, which we have called D. The intersection operation will be the "multiplication" operation of the number system we are constructing. We shall designate it by the symbol $\cap$.

38

The intersection of A and B will be written as $A \cap B$, and is read as "A intersection B." Then we see that $A \cap B = D$. When two subsets have no elements in common, their intersection is the empty set. The method of finding intersections is shown in the following examples:

$$I \cap C = \{x, y, z\} \cap \{y, z\} = \{y, z\} = C$$
$$A \cap D = \quad \{x, y\} \cap \{x\} = \{x\} = D$$
$$B \cap 0 = \quad \{x, z\} \cap \{\ \} = \{\ \} = 0$$
$$E \cap F = \quad \{y\} \cap \{z\} = \{\ \} = 0$$

The results of forming all possible intersections can be summarized in this table of intersections (the multiplication table for the number system we are constructing):

$\cap$	I	A	B	C	D	E	F	0
I	I	A	B	C	D	E	F	0
A	A	A	D	E	D	E	0	0
B	B	D	B	F	D	0	F	0
C	C	E	F	C	0	E	F	0
D	D	D	D	0	D	0	0	0
E	E	E	0	E	0	E	0	0
F	F	0	F	F	0	0	F	0
0	0	0	0	0	0	0	0	0

The Five Laws Are Obeyed

The operations "union" and "intersection" obey the five laws listed on pages 24-5. We can verify this fact by referring back to the meaning of these operations. Let us examine the laws one at a time, to see if they are obeyed.

39

1. *The commutative law of addition.* Union is our addition operation, so we must see whether $X \cup Y = Y \cup X$, where X and Y represent any subsets of I. $X \cup Y$ means the set that consists of those elements that are in X or Y. $Y \cup X$ means the set that consists of those elements that are in Y or X. These are obviously the same sets, so law number 1 is obeyed.

2. *The associative law for unions.* We must see whether $(X \cup Y) \cup Z = X \cup (Y \cup Z)$. The set $(X \cup Y) \cup Z$ is the set consisting of elements that are in X or Y, or in Z. The set $X \cup (Y \cup Z)$ is the set consisting of elements that are in X, or in Y or Z. These are obviously the same sets, so that law number 2 is obeyed.

3. *The commutative law of multiplication.* Intersection is our multiplication operation, so we must see whether $X \cap Y = Y \cap X$. $X \cap Y$ means the set consisting of elements that are in both X and Y. $Y \cap X$ means the set consisting of elements that are in both Y and X. These are obviously the same sets, so law number 3 is obeyed.

4. *The associative law for intersections.* $(X \cap Y) \cap Z$ means the set consisting of elements that are in X and Y, and also in Z. $X \cap (Y \cap Z)$ means the set consisting of elements that are in X, and also in Y and Z. Clearly, then $(X \cap Y) \cap Z = X \cap (Y \cap Z)$, and law number 4 is obeyed.

5. *The distributive law.* We must see if $X \cap (Y \cup Z) = (X \cap Y) \cup (X \cap Z)$. $X \cap (Y \cup Z)$ means the set consisting of elements that are in X and in Y or Z. $(X \cap Y) \cup (X \cap Z)$ means the set consisting of elements that are in X and Y, or in X and Z. These are clearly the same sets, so law number 5 is obeyed.

Since the five laws are obeyed, the system of subsets of I, with the operations union and intersection, forms a number system. Similar number systems can be constructed from the subsets of any given set. In the example just given, we started with a set that contains three elements, and found that it has eight subsets. As a result we obtained a number system that contained exactly eight members. Had we started with a different number of elements, we would have obtained a number system with a different number of members. For example, a set with two elements has four subsets. A set with four elements has sixteen subsets. A set with five elements has thirty-two subsets. In general, a set with n elements has 2^n subsets.

Zero and Unity Elements

The number system we have constructed has a zero element and a unity element. Since union is our addition operation, a zero element would have to have the property that when it is united with any element of the system, it leaves that element unchanged. A glance at the union table on page 38 shows that the empty set has this property. That is why we used the symbol 0 to represent it. Since intersection is our multiplication operation, a unity element would have to have the property that when it is intersected with any element of the system, it leaves that element unchanged. A glance at the intersection table on page 39 shows that the original set I has this property. We chose the symbol I to represent it because of its resemblance to the number 1.

Special Properties

The number system we have just constructed out of the subsets of $\{x, y, z\}$ has, as we have seen, some properties that it shares with the natural number system. These include obedience to the five laws, and possession of a zero element and a unity element. However, it also has some peculiar properties that are entirely unlike the properties of the natural number system. A few of these are noted here.

1. We can see from the tables that for any element X in the system, $X \cup X = X$, and $X \cap X = X$. That is, a subset united with itself yields the same subset, and a subset intersected with itself yields the same subset. In the natural number system, such an outcome is the exception rather than

the rule. $0 + 0 = 0$, but $2 + 2$ is not 2. $1 \cdot 1 = 1$, but $2 \cdot 2$ is not 2.

2. We have already observed that intersection is distributive with respect to union. It can also be verified that union is distributive with respect to intersection. That is, in the statement of the distributive law, union and intersection can change places. This, too, is unlike what we found in the natural number system. There, while multiplication is distributive with respect to addition, addition is not distributive with respect to multiplication.

3. For each subset in the system, we can find another one that contains just those elements that the first one does not. We call this second subset the *complement* of the first one, because, while they do not overlap (their intersection is 0), together they complete the original set (their union is I). If X is any subset in the system, we denote its complement by X'. In the system of subsets of $\{x, y, z\}$, $A = \{x, y\}$, so $A' = \{z\} = F$. Similarly, $B' = E$, $C' = D$, and $I' = 0$. The operation of "taking the complement" has the following properties:

$$X \cap X' = 0, X \cup X' = I; (X')' = X.$$

It also obeys the very useful law known as De Morgan's Rule: The complement of a union is the intersection of the complements; and the complement of an intersection is the union of the complements. Written out in symbols, the law says:

$$(X \cup Y)' = X' \cap Y'; (X \cap Y)' = X' \cup Y'.$$

The truth of the law can be observed by noting that a union consists of elements in one set *or* the other, an intersection consists of elements in one set *and* another, and a complement consists of the elements *not in* a particular set. Then De Morgan's rule says that "not in either X or Y" is the same as "not in X and not in Y"; and that "not in both X and Y" is the same as "not in X or not in Y." A little thought will show that these statements are correct.

The Algebra of Logic

The number system we have constructed in this chapter is only one of a whole family of number systems that have similar properties. They are called Boolean algebras. The type of structure that they represent is not just a mathematical curiosity. It has an important practical application in the study of logic, and in the design of electronic computers. In logic we study relationships among statements. The analysis of these relationships can be carried out in symbols in the following way: Let each proposition or statement be represented by a letter, such as p, q, or r. Use the symbol $\cup$ for "or," the symbol $\cap$ for "and," and the symbol $'$ for "not," as we already have done in the last paragraph. Use 0 for any statement that is false, and I for any statement that is true. With this notation, the class of statements and their logical relations becomes a Boolean algebra. Boolean algebras are named after the English mathematician, George Boole, who pioneered in the study of symbolic logic.

DO IT YOURSELF

1. Assign names to the subsets of the set $\{x, y\}$ as follows:
   $I = \{x, y\}, A = \{x\}, B = \{y\}, 0 = \{ \ \} = $ the empty set.
   a) Construct a table for the union operation for this system of subsets.
   b) Construct a table for the intersection operation.
2. Let I represent the set $\{a, b, c, d, e, f, g, h\}$.
   Let X represent the subset $\{a, b, c, d\}$.
   Let Y represent the subset $\{a, b, e, f, g\}$.
   a) What elements are in X', the complement of X in I?
   b) What elements are in Y', the complement of Y in I?
   c) What elements are in $X' \cup Y'$?
   d) What elements are in $X \cap Y$?
   e) What elements are in $(X \cap Y)'$?
   f) Compare your answers to c) and e) to show that
      $X' \cup Y' = (X \cap Y)'$.
3. List all the sixteen subsets of the set $\{a, b, c, d\}$.

CHAPTER III

New Numbers from Old

Questions That Have No Answers

IN OUR everyday use of the natural numbers, besides adding them and multiplying them, we sometimes have occasion to subtract them. The operation of subtraction can be defined in terms of addition. The symbol $5 - 3$ really asks us the question, "What natural number added to 3 gives 5?" Since the answer to the question is the number 2, we say $5 - 3 = 2$. We call the answer the *difference* between 5 and 3. The question can also be written in the form of an equation, $x + 3 = 5$, and the answer to the question is the solution to the equation.

Our success in finding the difference between 5 and 3 tempts us to try to find the difference between any two natural numbers chosen at random. But then we run into trouble. Suppose, for example, we try to find the difference between 3 and 5, written as $3 - 5$. First we have to interpret the symbol as a question. It asks us, "What natural number added to 5 gives 3?" Unfortunately, the answer is that there isn't any such number. In the natural number system, we cannot subtract any number from any other number. The only time subtraction is possible in that system is when the subtrahend is not larger than the minuend. If a and b stand for any natural numbers, then the expression $a - b$ doesn't always have a meaning. If we think of it as the question, "What natural number added to b gives a?", then it doesn't always have an answer. If we use the equation $x + b = a$, which asks the same question, then it does not always have a solution. This is a defect of the natural number system

44

that limits its usefulness. Because, although the question $3 - 5$ is meaningless for the natural number system, there are practical problems that lead to just such a question. For example, if the temperature is 3 degrees, what will it be after the mercury drops 5 degrees? It would be useful to have a number system which contains a number that can serve as the answer to this question. The defect of the natural number system that we have observed confronts us with a challenge. Can we construct a number system that does not have this defect? Can we build a number system in which subtraction is always possible for any pair of numbers taken in any order, so that a $a - b$ always has a meaning, and $x + b = a$ always has a solution? We find that we can.

Readers who have had high school algebra will remember that a system of numbers that includes "negative" as well as "positive" numbers is supposed to serve this purpose. But in their course in high school algebra, they were given this system as a finished product obeying certain mysterious rules such as, "the product of two negative numbers is a positive number." In what follows, we do not take the existence of such a number system for granted. We prove it exists by actually constructing it. We also remove the mystery surrounding its rules by actually deriving them from the familiar rules governing the system of natural numbers.

Families of Differences

To construct the improved number system, we use a rather interesting device. The symbol $a - b$ asks us a question which does not always have an answer. To make sure that it will have an answer in the new system, we let the question be its own answer! In effect we say, let each expression like $5 - 3$, or $3 - 5$, or $2 - 7$, represent a number in the new system. To justify calling these strange things numbers we shall have to define addition and multiplication operations for them, and then show that with these operations they really constitute a number system.

However, we run into some complications even before we take our first step in this direction. In the natural number system, $5 - 3$ does have an answer, and the answer is 2. But $2 - 0$, $3 - 1$, $4 - 2$, $6 - 4$, and an endless list of similar symbols also represent 2. So we cannot simply let each such symbol stand for a separate number in the new system. We would want all of these symbols to represent the *same* number, just as they do in the natural number system. We take care of this difficulty by using as the elements of our new number system, not single symbols written in the form of a "difference" between two natural numbers, but whole families of such differences. The first step is to establish a rule by which we can recognize when two such symbols belong to the same family. We get a clue to the rule we should use by examining the difference symbols that represent the number 2. The difference $3 - 1$ and the difference $6 - 4$ represent the same number. Notice that if we add the left number of each symbol to the right number of the other, we get the same sum: $3 + 4 = 6 + 1$. We shall use this relationship as the criterion for identifying differences that belong to the same family.

Now we are ready to carry out our construction step by step. First we take all possible ordered pairs of natural numbers, such as 7 and 5, 3 and 9, 15 and 1, and so on. Then we write the "difference" of the numbers in the pair, taken in a definite order. Since the difference does not always have a meaning in the natural number system, we shall not use an ordinary minus sign when we write it. We shall use the symbol $\sim$ instead, to remind us that this is really not subtraction of natural numbers, but merely a symbol suggested by subtraction. So we now have symbols like $7 \sim 5$, $3 \sim 9$, $15 \sim 1$, and so on, each of which will be called a "difference" between natural numbers.

Now we associate with each difference a whole family of differences in the following way: *The family belonging to a difference $a \sim b$ consists of all those differences $u \sim v$ for which $a + v = u + b$.* To designate the family that belongs to a difference we shall write that difference inside

46

parentheses. Thus $(a \sim b)$ means the family of differences that belongs to $a \sim b$. The symbol $(3 \sim 1)$ means the family of differences that belongs to $3 \sim 1$. We have already seen that the difference $6 \sim 4$ belongs to this family because $3 + 4 = 6 + 1$. We call these families of differences *integers*. They will be the elements of our new number system.

We observe immediately two characteristics of these families which we call integers:

1) A difference belongs to its own family. For example, $3 \sim 1$ belongs to $(3 \sim 1)$. This follows from the fact that $u \sim v$ belongs to $(a \sim b)$ if $a + v = u + b$. In this case, $a = 3$, $b = 1$, $u = 3$, and $v = 1$, and $3 + 1 = 3 + 1$. In general, $a \sim b$ belongs to $(a \sim b)$ because $a + b = a + b$.

2) If one of two differences belongs to the family of the other, then they have the same families. Suppose, for example, that $a \sim b$ belongs to the family $(c \sim d)$. Then we can show that every member of $(a \sim b)$ belongs to $(c \sim d)$, and vice versa. If $p \sim q$ belongs to $(a \sim b)$, then by the criterion for membership in a family, $a + q = p + b$. However, $a \sim b$ belongs to $(c \sim d)$, so $c + b = a + d$. Adding these two equalities, we get $a + b + c + q = a + b + p + d$. Taking away $a + b$ from both sides, we get $c + q = p + d$. But this is equivalent to saying that $p \sim q$ belongs to $(c \sim d)$, according to our criterion for membership in a family. This shows that any member of $(a \sim b)$ also belongs to $(c \sim d)$. A similar argument, going through the same chain of steps in reverse, shows that every member of $(c \sim d)$ also belongs to $(a \sim b)$. So the families $(a \sim b)$ and $(c \sim d)$ have the same memberships, and are therefore the same.

The second characteristic of these families called integers has these consequences: First, each difference $a \sim b$ belongs to one and only one integer. Secondly, an integer may be represented by putting on display inside parentheses any one of the differences that belong to it. So $(3 \sim 1)$, $(4 \sim 2)$, $(5 \sim 3)$ all represent the same integer. Thirdly, the criterion for membership in an integer can also serve as a test for equality of integers. That is, the integers $(a \sim b)$ and $(c \sim d)$ are equal if and only if $a + d = c + b$. For example, to prove that $(3 \sim 1) = (4 \sim 2)$, it is enough to observe that $3 + 2 = 4 + 1$.

Addition and Multiplication of Integers

Now we define addition and multiplication for the system of integers. We assign a sum to any ordered pair of integers by means of the following defining equation:

$$(a \sim b) + (c \sim d) = (a + c \sim b + d)$$

The symbol on the right hand side of this equation represents an integer, because, if a and c are natural numbers, $a + c$ is also a natural number. Similarly, $b + d$ is a natural number. Then $a + c \sim b + d$ is a difference of natural numbers, and there is an integer that belongs to it.

We assign a product to any ordered pair of integers by means of the following defining equation:

$$(a \sim b) \cdot (c \sim d) = (a \cdot c + b \cdot d \sim a \cdot d + b \cdot c)$$

Here, too, the right hand side represents an integer, because the symbol inside the parentheses represents a difference of two natural numbers.

Notice that to find the sum of two integers, we make use of the natural numbers whose differences are on display inside the parentheses representing these integers. This fact leads to a problem that we have to pay attention to. Each integer is a family of differences. Any member of a family might be put on display to represent it. If we pick another difference to represent each of the integers we are adding, will we still get the same sum? If we do not, our definition is useless. However, the definition was well chosen. If we follow the directions it gives for finding the sum of two integers, we arrive at *the same result* no matter which members of the integers are used to represent them. We shall not take the time to prove this fact here, but shall merely verify it for a particular case. Suppose we want to add $(5 \sim 3)$ and $(6 \sim 5)$. Using our definition, we find that

$$(5 \sim 3) + (6 \sim 5) = (5 + 6 \sim 3 + 5) = (11 \sim 8).$$

However, $(5 \sim 3)$ could also be represented by $(4 \sim 2)$, because $5 + 2 = 4 + 3$. Similarly, $(6 \sim 5)$ could also be represented by $(5 \sim 4)$, because $6 + 4 = 5 + 5$. If we apply our definition to these other representatives of the two integers, we find that

$$(4 \sim 2) + (5 \sim 4) = (4 + 5 \sim 2 + 4) = (9 \sim 6).$$

By using different representatives for the two integers we were adding, we got sums that look different. However, although they look different, the sums are the same.

$$(11 \sim 8) = (9 \sim 6), \text{ because } 11 + 6 = 9 + 8.$$

The same problem arises in connection with our definition for multiplication of integers. The definition makes use of a particular difference that belongs to each integer. But it can be shown that it does not matter which difference that belongs to an integer is chosen as its representative. They all lead to the same product anyhow. So there is no ambiguity in our definitions of addition and multiplication.

The Integers Form a Number System

We now have a system of elements called integers, with an addition operation and a multiplication operation defined for this system. To show that the integers form a number system, we have to prove that the operations obey the five laws listed on pages 24-5. As an example of how such a proof is carried out, we give the details of the proof for the commutative law of addition. Let $(a \sim b)$ be any integer, and $(c \sim d)$ any other integer. We must show that $(a \sim b) + (c \sim d) = (c \sim d) + (a \sim b)$. Applying our definition of addition of integers, we find that $(a \sim b) + (c \sim d) = (a + c \sim b + d)$, while $(c \sim d) + (a \sim b) = (c + a \sim d + b)$. But natural numbers obey the commutative law for addition, so $a + c = c + a$, and $b + d = d + b$. This shows that $(a + c \sim b + d)$ and $(c + a \sim d + b)$ are the same integer. Therefore, $(a \sim b) + (c \sim d) = (c \sim d) + (a \sim b)$, and the commutative law for addition of integers is true. The other four laws are proved by similar arguments, using the definitions of addition and multiplication of integers, and the fact that natural numbers are known to obey the five laws.

Zero and Unity

Let us add the integer $(0 \sim 0)$ to any other integer $(a \sim b)$. Following the definition of addition, we find that $(0 \sim 0) + (a \sim b) = (0 + a \sim 0 + b) = (a \sim b)$, since $0 + a = a$, and $0 + b = b$. In other words, when $(0 \sim 0)$ is added to any other integer, it leaves that integer unchanged. Therefore $(0 \sim 0)$ is a zero element for the system of integers. The integer $(0 \sim 0)$, like any other integer, is a family of differences, and may be represented by any one of these differences. We can identify what these differences look like by using the criterion for belonging to an integer. The difference $x \sim y$ belongs to the family of differences $(0 \sim 0)$, if and only if $0 + y = x + 0$, or $y = x$. That is, a difference belongs to the integer $(0 \sim 0)$ if and only if the left number and the right number are equal. So $(1 \sim 1)$, $(2 \sim 2)$, $(3 \sim 3)$, and so on, are other ways of writing the zero element in the system of integers.

Let us see how the integer $(1 \sim 0)$ behaves under multiplication. Following the definition of multiplication, we find that $(1 \sim 0) \cdot (a \sim b) = (1 \cdot a + 0 \cdot b \sim 1 \cdot b + 0 \cdot a) = (a + 0 \sim b + 0) = (a \sim b)$. In other words, when $(1 \sim 0)$ is multiplied by any other integer, it leaves that integer unchanged. So $(1 \sim 0)$ is a unity element for the system of integers. It may also be written in the form $(a + 1 \sim a)$, where a is any natural number. This follows from the test for equality of integers, because $a + 1 + 0 = 1 + a$.

The Negative of an Integer

Our purpose in constructing the system of integers was to find a number system in which an equation of the form $X + B = A$ always has a solution. To show that we have achieved our purpose, we have to introduce a new concept, the concept of the *negative* of a number. We say that one number is the negative of another if the sum of the two numbers is zero. In the natural number system, there is only one number that has a negative. That number is 0, and it is its own negative, because $0 + 0 = 0$. No other natural number has a negative, because if a natural number that is different from 0 is added to any other natural number, the sum is different from 0. However, the system of integers is altogether different in this respect: In the system of integers, *every* number has a negative. We prove this fact by actually producing the negative of any integer. Let $(a \sim b)$ be any integer. Then $(b \sim a)$ is its negative, because $(a \sim b) + (b \sim a) = (a + b \sim b + a) =$ the zero integer, because, in the difference on display inside the parentheses, the left number is equal to the right number. Because every integer has a negative, we introduce a special symbol to mean "negative of." The minus sign is used for this purpose. If A stands for an integer, then $-A$ is used to represent the negative of A.

Now we are prepared to show that the equation $X + B = A$ always has a solution, if X, A, and B stand for integers. We have used capital letters here to represent integers, so that we would not confuse them with natural numbers. Each integer is a family of differences of natural numbers, so the equation can also be written in this form: $(x \sim y) + (c \sim d) = (a \sim b)$. We solve the equation by adding the negative of $(c \sim d)$ to both sides. We get

$$(x \sim y) + (c \sim d) + (d \sim c) = (a \sim b) + (d \sim c).$$

But the sum of $(c \sim d)$ and $(d \sim c)$ is the zero integer. And the zero integer added to $(x \sim y)$ leaves it unchanged. So we have $(x \sim y) = (a \sim b) + (d \sim c) = (a + d \sim b + c)$. For example, to solve $(x \sim y) + (8 \sim 1) = (3 \sim 2)$, add $(1 \sim 8)$ to both sides. Then we get $(x \sim y) = (4 \sim 10)$.

On page 44 we saw that solving $X + B = A$ was another way of saying subtract B from A. Since, in the system of integers, the equation always has a solution, it means that subtraction is always possible in that system. In fact, our

51

method for solving the equation suggests an appropriate definition for the subtraction of integers: To *subtract* an integer, means to add its negative. This definition makes sense in the system of integers, where every number has a negative. We could not have defined subtraction of natural numbers in the same way, because in the system of natural numbers, it is not true that every number has a negative.

We Still Have the Natural Numbers

Among the integers, there are some special integers like $(0 \sim 0)$, $(1 \sim 0)$, $(2 \sim 0)$, $(3 \sim 0)$, and so on, which are written by putting on display a difference in which the number on the right is 0. These special integers are called *positive* integers. They can be placed in one-to-one correspondence with the natural numbers by pairing off 0 with $(0 \sim 0)$, 1 with $(1 \sim 0)$, 2 with $(2 \sim 0)$, and so on. In general, in this correspondence, each natural number a is matched with the positive integer $(a \sim 0)$.

Now let us see what happens when we add or multiply any two positive integers, $(a \sim 0)$ and $(b \sim 0)$. For the sum, we get $(a \sim 0) + (b \sim 0) = (a + b \sim 0)$. So the sum of two positive integers is a positive integer. For the product, we get $(a \sim 0) \cdot (b \sim 0) = (a \cdot b + 0 \cdot 0 \sim a \cdot 0 + 0 \cdot b) = (a \cdot b \sim 0)$. So the product of two positive integers is a positive integer. Moreover, the sum of the integers matched with a and b is the integer matched with $a + b$; and the product of the integers matched with a and b is the integer matched with $a \cdot b$. That is, under the one-to-one correspondence the sum of the images of two natural numbers is the image of their sum; and the product of the images is the image of the product.

So the positive integers are isomorphic to the natural numbers. Because of the isomorphism, they can be used instead of the natural numbers, just as Roman numerals can be used instead of Arabic numerals. In this sense, we say that the positive integers are the "same" as the natural numbers. We take advantage of the isomorphism by using the notation for natural numbers as an abbreviated notation for the positive integers. In this abbreviated notation 0 represents $(0 \sim 0)$, 1 represents $(1 \sim 0)$, and so on.

Since the system of integers includes the positive integers which are just "like" the natural numbers, they constitute an *extension* of the natural number system. Using the system of integers instead of the system of natural numbers gives us a double advantage: We eliminate a defect of the natural number system, without losing the natural numbers themselves.

The Negative Integers

Every integer can be represented by a difference in which either the left number or the right number is 0. This can be done by simply subtracting from each of these natural numbers the smaller of the two. The result will be a difference that belongs to the integer, and so can be used to represent it. For example, the integer $(8 \sim 3)$ is equal to $(5 \sim 0)$. We know they are equal because $8 + 0 = 5 + 3$. The integer $(3 \sim 8)$ is equal to $(0 \sim 5)$, because $3 + 5 = 0 + 8$. So every integer may be written in the form $(a \sim 0)$ or $(0 \sim a)$. Those that can be written in the form $(a \sim 0)$ are the positive integers. Those that can be written in the form $(0 \sim a)$ are called negative integers. Each of them is the negative of a positive integer. Using the minus sign as the symbol for "negative of," we get an abbreviated notation for them, too, by writing $-a$ for $(0 \sim a)$.

This is the form in which students are introduced to them for the first time in courses in elementary algebra. The familiar rules for calculating with these symbols can all be derived from our definitions for the addition and multiplication of integers. For example, the rule that the product of two negative integers is a positive integer can be proved as follows: $(0 \sim a) \cdot (0 \sim b) = (0 \cdot 0 + a \cdot b \sim 0 \cdot b + a \cdot 0) = (a \cdot b \sim 0)$, which is positive.

The positive integers, being essentially carbon copies of the natural numbers, can be represented as the natural numbers were on page 29, by points on the half-line that lies to the right of the 0. We can represent the negative numbers pictorially, too, by putting them on the other half of the line, on the other side of 0. Arranging them on a line suggests that we can talk about larger and smaller integers, just as we were able to talk about larger and smaller natural numbers. We give a meaning to the term larger as applied to integers by agreeing that one integer will be considered larger than another if it lies to the right of it on the line on which the integers are represented as points in the diagram below. The term can also be defined without reference to the picture. If a and b are two different integers, we say that a is larger than b if $a - b$ is positive. It is understood here that $a - b$ means $a + $ the negative of b, in ac-

cordance with the definition of subtraction of integers given on page 52. On the basis of this definition, 2 is larger than -7, because $2 - (-7) = 2 + 7 = 9$, which is positive. The integer -4 is larger than -5, because $-4 - (-5) = -4 + 5 = 1$, which is positive.

The Integers Form a Group

Before we proceed to any further extension of our number system, let us stay with the system of integers for a while to observe some of its properties. We shall find within the system of integers examples of some of the structures that form the typical subject matter of modern mathematics.

We have two binary operations defined for the system of integers, addition and multiplication. Let us disregard multiplication, and list some of the properties the system has in relation to the operation of addition alone. We observe these characteristics: 1) The operation of addition is associative. 2) The system contains a zero element. 3) For every integer a in the system, its negative, $-a$, is also in the system. These characteristics make the system of integers an example of the type of structure that is known as a "group." In fact, with a slight change in notation, introduced in order to give them a more general form, these characteristics make up the definition of a group.

As we did once before on page 28, let us designate the binary operation by the symbol *. Zero is an example of an identity element, and if we designate it now by the letter e, the property that $0 + x = x + 0 = x$ can be written in the more general notation as follows: $e * x = x * e = x$. Instead of the word "negative," let us substitute the word "inverse," and designate the inverse of a by a^{-1}. In this notation, the fact that the sum of any integer and its negative is zero takes this form: $a * a^{-1} = a^{-1} * a = e$.

Here, then, is the definition of a group: A group is a system of elements for which a binary operation * is defined, and which has these properties: 1) The operation * is associative. 2) The system contains an identity element e, with the property that, if x is any element in the system, $e * x = x * e = x$. 3) For every element a in the system, its inverse a^{-1} is also in the system, with the property that $a * a^{-1} = a^{-1} * a = e$. The word "negative" is used for an inverse only in the special case where the operation is designated by $+$ and is called "addition."

Another Example of a Group

The type of structure known as a group has been singled out for special study by mathematicians because it is found in many places. The system of integers is only one of a multitude of systems that have a group structure. It happens to be a group that contains an infinite number of elements. But there are also groups that contain a finite number of elements. As an example of a finite group, let us examine the group of "symmetries" of an equilateral triangle.

An equilateral triangle has equal sides and equal angles. The symmetries of the triangle are motions that bring it into coincidence with itself. To get acquainted with these motions, it is best to see them in action as applied to a model. So, before reading the paragraphs that follow, cut

an equilateral triangle out of paper, and label its vertices
A, B, and C, as shown in the diagram. Enter the labels on
the reverse side of the paper, too, so that the vertices can be
identified even when the triangle is turned over.

Let us begin with the triangle placed on a level surface
so that one side, say BC, is horizontal, and the opposite
vertex A lies above BC, as shown in the diagram below.

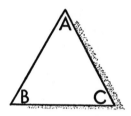

Now, as we discover motions that bring the triangle into
coincidence with itself, we shall assign a name to each one.
One motion that will qualify is a clockwise rotation of 120
degrees around the center of the triangle. The result of
such a rotation is to put B in the place of A, A in the place
of C, and C in the place of B. Let us call this rotation P.
Another motion that qualifies is a clockwise rotation of 240
degrees. It puts C in the place of A, B in the place of C, and
A in the place of B. Let us call it Q. Another "motion" that
qualifies is a clockwise rotation of 0 degrees. This, of course,
involves no movement of the triangle at all, and leaves A
in the place of A, B in the place of B and C in the place of
C. We shall call it I.

Before we go any further, let us make an agreement. We
shall consider two motions as being the "same" if they have
the same effect. A clockwise rotation of 360 degrees has the
same effect as a rotation of 0 degrees, so it, too, will be
called I. A counterclockwise rotation of 120 degrees has the
same effect as a clockwise rotation of 240 degrees, so it, too,
will be called Q. Similarly, a counterclockwise rotation of
240 degrees is the same as P.

There are three more motions that can bring the triangle
into coincidence with itself. In one of them, we flip the tri-

56

Motion	Symbol	First position	Final position
No motion	**I**		
Rotate 120° clockwise	**P**		
Rotate 240° clockwise	**Q**		
Flip over, keeping top vertex fixed	**R**		
Flip over, keeping left vertex fixed	**S**		
Flip over, keeping right vertex fixed	**T**		

angle over to bring the bottom face up, while leaving the top vertex where it is. If we start with A at the top, B at the left, and C at the right, this motion puts A in its own place, and makes B and C change places. Let us call this motion R. A similar motion that keeps the vertex on the left fixed, while the top vertex and the vertex on the right change places, will be called S. One which keeps the vertex on the right fixed, while the top vertex and the vertex on the left change places, will be called T.

We now have a system consisting of six elements, I, P, Q, R, S, and T. We define a binary operation $*$ for this system as follows: If A and B represent any two of these motions, the product $A * B$ is the motion that results when the two motions are performed one right after the other, with B

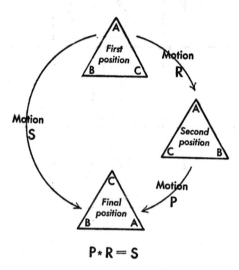

$$P * R = S$$

performed first, and A taking over where B leaves off. For example, $P * R$ means first perform R, then P. If we start with vertex A at the top, B at the left, and C at the right, motion R leaves A at the top, and makes B and C change places. Then, from this position, motion P rotates the triangle 120 degrees clockwise. As a result, A moves to the position on the right, B moves to the position on the left, and C moves to the top. The effect is the same as if only the single motion S had been used. So $P * R = S$. If we pick any two of the six motions at random, and perform one after the other, we find that the result is always one of the original six motions. The results of performing the operation * can be summarized in the multiplication table shown below, where the motion that is performed first, and is written on the right hand side in a product, is listed at the top of the table, and the motion that is performed second, and is written on the left hand side in a product, is written at the side.

MULTIPLICATION TABLE
FOR SYMMETRIES OF THE TRIANGLE

*	I	P	Q	R	S	T
I	I	P	Q	R	S	T
P	P	Q	I	S	T	R
Q	Q	I	P	T	R	S
R	R	T	S	I	Q	P
S	S	R	T	P	I	Q
T	T	S	R	Q	P	I

To show that the symmetries of the triangle form a group, we have to prove that the three requirements for a group are satisfied. 1) The operation * is associative. That is, if A, B, and C are any three motions in the system, $A * (B * C) = (A * B) * C$. This can be verified from the table, or from the fact that both symbols, $A * (B * C)$, and $(A * B) * C$ require that C be performed first, B second, and A third, so that both lead to the same result. The parentheses here signify no more than a pause between motions. 2) The system has an identity element. In fact I is the identity element, because the table shows that if X stands for any element, $I * X = X * I = X$. 3) For every element in the system, there is an inverse element that is also in the system. The inverse of P is Q, and the inverse of Q is P, because $P * Q = Q * P = I$. Each of the elements, I, R, S, and T is its own inverse, because $I * I = I$, $R * R = I$,

$S * S = I$, and $T * T = I$. Therefore the symmetries of the triangle, with the operation * as defined, form a group.

Not All Groups Are Commutative

We see from the multiplication table for the group of symmetries that $P * R = S$, and that $R * P = T$. Therefore $P * R$ is not equal to $R * P$. The operation * in this group does not obey the commutative law. On the other hand, in the system of integers, which forms a group with the operation $+$, the operation is commutative. A group which obeys the commutative law is called a commutative group. It is also called an *abelian* group in honor of one of the pioneers in the study of groups, Niels Henrik Abel, who died at the age of 27 in 1829. It is now the custom to use the symbol $+$ to represent the binary operation in a group only if it is a commutative or abelian group. If the plus sign is used to designate the operation, then the word *zero* is used instead of *identity*, and the word *negative* is used instead of *inverse*.

Although the system of integers is the most commonly used system that has a group structure, it was not the first system to have its group structure analyzed. The first groups that were studied extensively were finite groups, like the group of symmetries of the triangle. They came up in the theory of equations, as studied by the methods of the French mathematician Evariste Galois. Galois recorded his findings in 1832 in a paper that he wrote the night before he was killed in a duel at the age of 21. After being neglected for about thirty years, they were saved from obscurity and extended by other mathematicians. Since then, the concept of a group has invaded every branch of mathematics.

The Integers Form a Ring

To observe the group structure of the system of integers, we disregarded the operation of multiplication. Now, if we put multiplication back into the picture, we find in the system of integers an example of another structure that plays an important part in modern mathematics, a *ring*. A system of elements is called a ring if there are two binary operations defined for the system, and they have these properties: 1) Both operations are associative. 2) The system is an abelian group with respect to one of the operations. This operation is designated by +, and is called addition. 3) The other operation is distributive with respect to addition. If we call it multiplication, and represent it by the usual symbol for "times," then the distributive law takes this form: $a \cdot (b + c) = a \cdot b + a \cdot c$; and $(b + c) \cdot a = b \cdot a + c \cdot a$. It is necessary to state the distributive law in two parts in this way, because the multiplication operation need not be commutative, so multiplication by a from the left is not the same as multiplication by a from the right.

The fact that the system of integers is a ring follows from the properties of the system that we have already seen.

Multiplication by Zero

One of the familiar rules of arithmetic that we use every day when we work with natural numbers is that zero times any number gives a product equal to zero. This rule turns out to be true in the system of integers as well. In fact, we can show that it has to be true *in any system that has a ring structure*. In any ring, if x is any element, and 0 is its zero element, $x + 0 = x$. Now multiply both sides of this equation by any other element in the ring, say y. Then we have $y \cdot (x + 0) = y \cdot x$. By the distributive law in the ring, we can replace $y \cdot (x + 0)$ by $y \cdot x + y \cdot 0$, so we get $y \cdot x + y \cdot 0 = y \cdot x$. Since the ring is a group with respect to addition, the element $y \cdot x$ has a negative, $-(y \cdot x)$. Let us add this negative to both sides of the equation. We get $-(y \cdot x) + y \cdot x + y \cdot 0 = -(y \cdot x) + y \cdot x$. But $-(y \cdot x) + y \cdot x = 0$, from the definition of a negative. So we now have $0 + y \cdot 0 = 0$. But since 0 is a zero element for addition, $0 + y \cdot 0$ can be replaced by $y \cdot 0$. This leads to the conclusion that $y \cdot 0 = 0$.

Hidden Groups and Rings

The group structure and ring structure that we have observed so far in the system of integers lie on the surface, we might say, because they embrace the system as a whole. However, there are more group and ring structures hidden within the system of integers as substructures. We shall produce some examples for examination.

Suppose we divide the integer 6 by 3. The quotient is 2, which is also an integer. Then 6 can be written as $2 \cdot 3$. There are other integers that can also be written as some integer times 3. For example, $-9 = -3 \cdot 3$. All such integers are called integral multiples of 3. The integral multiples of 3 form the set {0, 3, −3, 6, −6, 9, −9, 12, −12, ...}. The dots inside the brace indicate that there are many more members of the set besides those that are listed. A characteristic of all integral multiples of 3 is that when we divide them by 3, the remainder is 0.

The integers which are not multiples of 3 can be divided into two families. One family consists of those that are 1 more than an integral multiple of 3. For example, $7 = 6 + 1$, and $-5 = -6 + 1$, so 7 and −5 both belong to this family. Members of this family have the characteristic that when we divide them by 3, the remainder is 1. The other family consists of those integers that are 2 more than an integral multiple of 3. For example, $8 = 6 + 2$, and $-4 = -6 + 2$, so 8 and −4 belong to this family. Members of this family have the characteristic that when we divide them by 3, the remainder is 2. All integers therefore fall into one of three classes, depending on whether the remainder, when we divide by 3, is 0, 1, or 2. We call these classes *residue classes* modulo 3. For convenience in talking about them, we shall designate each class by the remainder which is characteristic of it. Here, then, are the three classes:

$$0 \text{ class: } \left\{ \begin{array}{llllll} 0, & 3, & 6, & 9, & 12, & \ldots \ldots \\ & -3, & -6, & -9, & -12, & \ldots \ldots \end{array} \right\}$$

$$1 \text{ class: } \left\{ \begin{array}{lllll} 1, & 4, & 7, & 10, & 13, \ldots \\ -2, & -5, & -8, & -11, & -14, \ldots \end{array} \right\}$$

$$2 \text{ class: } \left\{ \begin{matrix} 2, & 5, & 8, & 11, & 14, \dots \\ -1, & -4, & -7, & -10, & -13, \dots \end{matrix} \right\}$$

The 0 class has some interesting properties. Notice first that if we add any two members of the 0 class, the sum is itself a member of the 0 class. For example, $3 + (-6) = -3$. This is not true of the other two classes. For example, although 1 and 4 belong to the 1 class, their sum, $1 + 4 = 5$, which is not in the 1 class. Similarly, although 2 and 5 belong to the 2 class, their sum, $2 + 5 = 7$, which is not in the 2 class. Therefore, addition is a binary operation for the 0 class, but not for the 1 class or the 2 class. (Recall that a binary operation is defined for a set only by a mapping that associates with each pair of elements in the set another element *in the same set.*) Since addition is associative for the whole system of integers, it is surely associative when used with the members of the 0 class alone.

Notice, secondly, that the 0 class contains the identity element for addition, namely, 0. Moreover, for every element in the 0 class, its negative also belongs to the class. Therefore the 0 class satisfies all the requirements for being a group in its own right. In fact, since addition is commutative, it is even an abelian group. Because it is a group that is a subset of the larger group of integers, it is called a subgroup of the group of integers. The other two residue classes modulo 3 cannot qualify as subgroups with respect to addition, because, as we have seen, addition is not even a binary operation for them.

We can say even more about the 0 class. If we multiply any two members of the 0 class, the product is itself a member of the 0 class. So that multiplication is also a binary operation for this class. Moreover, it obeys the distributive law, so the 0 class satisfies all the requirements for being a ring in its own right. It is called a subring of the ring of integers.

We can say still more about the 0 class. If we multiply any member of the 0 class by *any integer,* whether it is in the class or not, the product is a member of the 0 class. For

63

example, $4 \cdot 3 = 12$, which is in the 0 class, although 4 is not. A subring which has this property is called an *ideal,* so the 0 class modulo 3 is an ideal in the ring of integers.

The 0 class, considered as a ring, differs in one very important way from the ring of integers. It does not contain the number 1, which is the unity element for multiplication. So we see it is possible for a ring to be with or without a unity element.

The Arithmetic of Residue Classes

We are now going to construct a new number system whose elements are the residue classes modulo 3. To do so, we must define what we mean by addition and multiplication of these classes. We define addition as follows: To add two residue classes, pick one member from each class, and add these members. The class to which the sum belongs will be called the sum of those residue classes. For example, to add the 1 class and the 2 class, we might add 1 (chosen from the 1 class) to 2 (chosen from the 2 class). The sum is 3, which belongs to the 0 class. Therefore the 1 class plus the 2 class equals the 0 class. Our definition allows us a free choice in picking the numbers in each class that we will add. However, it makes no difference which ones we choose, because all members of the same class have the same remainder when divided by 3. Adding a representative from each of two classes is like adding their remainders, and the result is the same no matter which representative is chosen.

We can prove this fact for the illustration being given in this way: Any number in the 1 class is of the form $3a + 1$. Any number in the 2 class is of the form $3b + 2$. When we add them, we get $3a + 1 + 3b + 2 = 3a + 3b + 3 = 3(a + b + 1)$, that is a multiple of 3, which is in the 0 class. For the sake of brevity, let us now drop the word class from the name of each class, and simply refer to them as 0, 1, and 2. Then we get the following addition table for residue classes modulo 3:

+	0	1	2
0	0	1	2
1	1	2	0
2	2	0	1

We define multiplication in the same way: To find the product of two residue classes, multiply any member of one class by any member of the other. The class to which the product belongs is the product of the classes. For example, to multiply the 2 class by the 2 class, multiply 2 (chosen from the 2 class) by 5 (chosen from the 2 class). The product is 10, which belongs to the 1 class. So the 2 class times the 2 class equals the 1 class. As in the case of addition, it makes no difference which member of each class is chosen for carrying out the operation. Here, too, we drop the word class from the name of each class, and record the products in the following multiplication table for residue classes modulo 3:

·	0	1	2
0	0	0	0
1	0	1	2
2	0	2	1

With these tables for addition and multiplication, the residue classes modulo 3 obey the five laws. Therefore they make up a number system consisting of only 3 elements. This number system is also both a group and a ring. It is a group with respect to addition, because 1) it contains a zero element, viz., the 0 class, and 2) for every element in the system, there is a negative in the system, too. The 0 class is a zero element, because, as the addition table shows, that class added to any other class leaves it unchanged: $0 + 0 = 0$, $0 + 1 = 1$, and $0 + 2 = 2$. The negative of 0 is 0. The negative of 1 is 2, and vice versa, because $1 + 2 = 2 + 1 = 0$. The group is abelian, because the addition operation is commutative. The system is also a ring, because, besides being an abelian group, it has a multiplication operation which is distributive with respect to addition. For example, $2(1 + 2) = 2(0) = 0$, and $2 \cdot 1 + 2 \cdot 2 = 2 + 1 = 0$. Therefore $2(1 + 2) = 2 \cdot 1 + 2 \cdot 2$.

Quotient Groups

The group that we have just observed contained as its elements a subgroup of the system of integers (the 0 class), and certain companion sets, the 1 class and the 2 class. The companion sets can be obtained from the subgroup by adding to each member of the subgroup some element that is not in it. For example, by adding 1 to each of the elements in the 0 class, we get all the elements of the 1 class. In fact, if we add any single member of the 1 class to each of the elements in the 0 class, we get all the members of the 1 class. Similarly, if we add any member of the 2 class to each of the elements of the 0 class, we get all the members of the 2 class. Companion classes that have this relationship to a subgroup are called its *cosets*. When a subgroup and its cosets are themselves elements of a group, the group they form is called a *quotient group*.

If we look back to the table for multiplication of the symmetries of a triangle (page 59), we shall find another example of a subgroup, its cosets, and a quotient group that they form. Here, of course, the group operation will be $*$ instead of $+$. Notice, first, that when I, P, and Q are multiplied among themselves, the product is always I, or P, or Q. Therefore the operation $*$ is a binary operation for the subset $\{I, P, Q\}$. The identity element I is in this subset, and the inverse of every element in the subset is also in the subset. In fact, the inverse of I is I, the inverse of P is Q, and the inverse of Q is P. Therefore the subset $\{I, P, Q\}$

66

forms a subgroup with the operation *. Its coset is the set $\{R, S, T\}$.

Now let us assign a short name to each of these sets, by writing $G = \{I, P, Q\}$, and $H = \{R, S, T\}$. We can define an operation * on the system whose elements are G and H as follows. To multiply one set by another, pick an element from each set, and multiply them. For example, take P (from G) * S (from H). The product is T, which is in H. The set to which the product belongs will be called the product of the sets. Therefore $G * H = H$. As in the case of residue classes, it turns out that the product comes out the same no matter which representative we choose from each class to carry out the operation. The products we get can be summarized in this multiplication table:

*	G	H
G	G	H
H	H	G

In this system of two elements, G is an identity element for the operation *, because $G * G = G$, and $G * H = H * G = H$. Also, there is an inverse for every element. In fact, each element is its own inverse, because $G * G = G$, and $H * H = G$, which is the identity element. Therefore the subgroup G and the coset H form a quotient group of the group of symmetries of the triangle. In this case, we can see why it is called a quotient group. The group of symmetries has 6 elements, the subgroup G has 3 elements, and the quotient group has $6 \div 3 = 2$ elements. Not every subgroup, together with its cosets, will form a quotient group. Galois was the first to identify the special kind of subgroups that have this property. They are known as normal subgroups. In an abelian group all subgroups are normal.

We saw that the residue classes modulo 3 form a ring as well as a group. It is an example of a *quotient ring*. Just as in a group, a special kind of subgroup with cosets forms a quotient group, in a ring, a special kind of ideal with its cosets form a quotient ring. In a ring in which the multiplication is commutative, all ideals have this property.

Residue Classes Modulo 6

We formed the residue classes modulo 3 by classifying the integers by the remainder you get when you divide by 3, using for this purpose only positive remainders that are less than 3, viz., 0, 1 and 2. If we use any other integer as divisor, we can divide the system of integers into residue classes modulo that integer in the same way. For example, when an integer is divided by 6, the remainder may be 0, 1, 2, 3, 4, or 5. This gives us six residue classes modulo 6. As we did in the case of residue classes modulo 3, let us use the remainder associated with each class as the name of the class. If we define addition and multiplication of residue classes the same way we did before, we get these addition and multiplication tables:

+	0	1	2	3	4	5
0	0	1	2	3	4	5
1	1	2	3	4	5	0
2	2	3	4	5	0	1
3	3	4	5	0	1	2
4	4	5	0	1	2	3
5	5	0	1	2	3	4

·	0	1	2	3	4	5
0	0	0	0	0	0	0
1	0	1	2	3	4	5
2	0	2	4	0	2	4
3	0	3	0	3	0	3
4	0	4	2	0	4	2
5	0	5	4	3	2	1

With these tables, the residue classes modulo 6 form a ring. This ring has a peculiar feature that it does not share with the ring of integers. In the ring of integers, the only time a product of two elements equals 0 is when one of the multipliers is itself 0. On the other hand, in the ring of residue classes modulo 6, $2 \cdot 3 = 0$, and neither 2 nor 3 is itself zero. Non-zero elements, like 2 and 3, which when multiplied give a zero product are called *zero divisors*. The ring of integers has no zero divisors, but the ring of residue classes modulo 6 does have zero divisors.

The absence of zero divisors in the ring of integers is the basis for one of the very important rules we all learned in elementary high school algebra, the cancellation law of multiplication. We learned that if $2 \cdot x = 2 \cdot 3$, we may cancel the 2 on both sides of the equation, and conclude that $x = 3$. The argument that proves this is correct proceeds as follows: Add the negative of $2 \cdot 3$ to both sides of the equation. This gives us $2 \cdot x - 2 \cdot 3 = 0$. By using the distributive law, we get $2 \cdot x - 2 \cdot 3 = 2 \, (x - 3)$. Therefore $2 \cdot (x - 3) = 0$. This statement tells us that the product of two integers equals 0. This can happen only if one of the multipliers is 0. Since 2 is not 0, the other multiplier, $x - 3$, must be 0. Therefore x has to be 3. In the ring of residue classes modulo 6, this whole argument breaks down, because there *are* zero divisors in the system. That is, a product can be equal to 0, without either of the multipliers being equal to 0. Consequently, the cancellation law of multiplication is not obeyed in this system. In fact, in this system, if $2 \cdot x = 2$, we cannot conclude that $x = 1$. The multiplication table shows that while $x = 1$ is one possible solution to the equation, $x = 4$ is another solution, because $2 \cdot 4 = 2$.

Mapping Group into Group

We can set up a mapping of the group of integers into the group of residue classes modulo 3 by assigning to each integer in the system of integers the residue class that it belongs to, as shown in the table:

$$0 \rightarrow 0$$
$$1 \rightarrow 1$$
$$2 \rightarrow 2$$
$$3 \rightarrow 0$$
$$4 \rightarrow 1$$
$$5 \rightarrow 2$$
$$6 \rightarrow 0$$

By this mapping, 0, 3, 6, 9, and 12, for example, have the 0 class as their image; 1, 4, 7, 10, and 13 have the 1 class as their image; and 2, 5, 8, and 14 have the 2 class as their image. The mapping is clearly a many-to-one mapping. It has the interesting property of *preserving the operation* that is defined for the group. That is, the image of a sum is the sum of the images. For example, the image of 3 is 0, and the image of 4 is 1. The sum of 3 and 4 is 7, and its image is 1, which is the sum of the images 0 and 1. A mapping like this, of one group into another, which preserves the group operation is called a *group homomorphism.* Where it is a many-to-one mapping it is like collapsing or telescoping the group to make it fit into a smaller one. If we consider the system of integers and the system of residue classes modulo 3 as rings, the same mapping preserves not only the group operation of addition, but also the other ring operation, multiplication. For this reason, it is also an example of a *ring homomorphism* (one which preserves the operations in the ring).

When a group homomorphism of one group into another is a one-to-one correspondence, then it is a group *isomorphism.* Each element in one group is then paired off with one and only one element in the other. In that case, we say that the two groups are isomorphic to each other, or have the same structure. Two groups that are isomorphic to each other are really the same group structure dressed up in different clothes. We have an example of isomorphic groups in the group of residue classes modulo 3, and the subgroup $\{I, P, Q\}$ of the group of symmetries of the triangle. A mapping which matches them one-to-one, and preserves the group operation is shown below:

$$0 \longleftrightarrow I$$
$$1 \longleftrightarrow P$$
$$2 \longleftrightarrow Q$$
$$+ \longleftrightarrow *$$

If we take any true statement in one system, such as $1 + 2 = 0$, and replace each symbol by its image under the

70

mapping, we get a true statement in the other system. In the example shown, we get $P * Q = I$. In other words, the symbols used in the two systems are like two different languages that may be used for expressing the same ideas. The isomorphism printed above is the dictionary that allows us to translate from one language into the other.

DO IT YOURSELF

1. Using the definition of multiplication of integers given on page 48, prove that multiplication of integers is commutative by showing that

$$(a \sim b) \cdot (c \sim d) = (c \sim d) \cdot (a \sim b).$$

2. Using $(0 \sim a)$ and $(0 \sim b)$ to represent any two negative integers, prove that the sum of two negative integers is a negative integer.

3. Using $(0 \sim a)$ to represent any negative integer, and $(b \sim 0)$ to represent any positive integer, prove that the product of a negative integer and a positive integer is a negative integer.

4. A rearrangement of the numbers 1, 2, 3 is called a *permutation* of these numbers. Each rearrangement has the effect of replacing one number by another. For example, if the arrangement 123 is changed to 312, 1 is replaced by 3, 2 is replaced by 1, and 3 is replaced by 2. This permutation can be represented as a mapping:

$$1 \to 3$$
$$2 \to 1$$
$$3 \to 2$$

There are six possible permutations of three numbers. Call them I, A, B, C, D, E as follows:

I	A	B
$1 \to 1$	$1 \to 2$	$1 \to 3$
$2 \to 2$	$2 \to 3$	$2 \to 1$
$3 \to 3$	$3 \to 1$	$3 \to 2$

C	D	E
$1 \to 1$	$1 \to 3$	$1 \to 2$
$2 \to 3$	$2 \to 2$	$2 \to 1$
$3 \to 2$	$3 \to 1$	$3 \to 3$

Define the product of two permutations $X * Y$ as the result of performing Y first and X afterwards on the result of Y. How a product is identified is shown in the following example: To find $A * B$:

B:	A:		I:
$1 \to 3 \to 1$			$1 \to 1$
$2 \to 1 \to 2$		Result:	$2 \to 2$
$3 \to 2 \to 3$			$3 \to 3$

Therefore $A * B = I$.

a) Construct the multiplication table for the permutations I, A, B, C, D, E.

b) Prove that they form a group with the operation $*$.

c) Identify the subgroups of this group.

d) Show that this group of permutations is isomorphic to the group of symmetries of the triangle.

5. Use the associated remainders, 0, 1, 2, 3, 4 as the names of the residue classes modulo 5. Use the definitions of addition and multiplication given on pages 64-5 to construct addition and multiplication tables for these residue classes.

Use the tables to verify that $2 \cdot (1 + 2) = 2 \cdot 1 + 2 \cdot 2$ in this system. Does this system have zero divisors?

6. Show that the set of all even integers is a subgroup of the group of integers with respect to the operation $+$. Show that it is a subring of the ring of integers. Show that it is an ideal of the ring of integers. (See definitions, pages 63-4.)

CHAPTER IV

Numbers for Measuring

Another Defect to Overcome

THE natural number system has the defect that subtraction is not always possible in that system. To overcome this defect, we constructed the system of integers, an enlarged number system that includes the natural numbers, and in which subtraction *is* always possible. In this chapter we undertake another extension of the number system for a similar purpose. We find that the system of integers has the defect that *division* is not always possible within the system. To overcome this defect, we shall construct an enlarged number system that includes the integers, and in which division *is* (almost) always possible. The word "almost" has to be included in the statement of our goal, because, in the enlarged system, there will still be one number whose use as a divisor will be forbidden.

Just as subtraction of natural numbers was defined in terms of addition, division of integers may be defined in terms of multiplication. The symbol $\frac{-6}{2}$ really asks us the question, "What integer multiplied by 2 gives -6 as the product?" Since the answer to the question is -3, we say $\frac{-6}{2} = -3$. We call the symbol $\frac{-6}{2}$ the *quotient* of -6 and 2. We also refer to it as a *fraction*, and in this case it has meaning as another symbol for the integer -3. The question asked by the fraction $\frac{-6}{2}$ can also be written in the form of an equation, $2 \cdot x = -6$, and the answer to the question is the solution to the equation.

However, some fractions ask us a question that we cannot answer in the system of integers. For example, the fraction $\frac{2}{3}$ asks the question, "What number, when multiplied by 3, gives 2 as the product?" In the system of integers there isn't any such number. So, in the system of integers, the fraction $\frac{2}{3}$ has no meaning, and the equation $3 \cdot x = 2$ has no solution. This situation offers us a challenge similar to the one we faced in the last chapter. Can we build a number system in which division is always possible for any pair of numbers, so that $\frac{a}{b}$ always has a meaning, and $b \cdot x = a$ always has a solution?

Zero Is an Exception

We find that we can, provided that we agree not to use zero as a divisor. We can see the reason for this exclusion if we try to answer the question that is asked by a fraction that has 0 in the denominator. If the numerator *is not 0*, as in the fraction $\frac{2}{0}$, the fraction asks, "What number multiplied by 0 gives 2 as the product?" We hope to make the enlarged number system a ring. And in a ring, as we saw on page 61, zero times any other number gives a product equal to zero. Then the answer to the question will have to be "No number." On the other hand, if the numerator of the fraction *is 0*, the situation is even worse. Then the fraction $\frac{0}{0}$ asks, "What number multiplied by 0 will give 0 as a product?" The answer to this question would be, "any number." In fact, even in the system of integers, this would be the answer. We would like the fractions in our expanded number system not to overreach themselves. We want each fraction to stand for *one and only one number*. Since the fraction $\frac{2}{0}$ stands for no

74

number, and the fraction $\frac{0}{0}$ stands for too many numbers,
we exclude them as legitimate fractions. So, from now on, whenever we talk about a fraction, it will be understood that the denominator may not be 0.

Families of Fractions

To construct the new number system, we use the same device that was employed in the last chapter. To be sure that the question asked by the fraction $\frac{a}{b}$ (where b is not 0) always has an answer, we shall let the question be its own answer. We shall let each fraction represent a number in the new system. However, the numbers in this system will not be single fractions. Just as each number in the system of integers is a *family of differences* of natural numbers, each number in the system we are now constructing will be a *family of fractions or quotients* of integers. This is made necessary by the fact that, even among fractions that have a meaning in the system of integers, many fractions can represent the same number. For example, $\frac{3}{1}, \frac{6}{2}, \frac{9}{3}, \frac{12}{4}$, and many others represent the number 3, so we shall have to put them together into one family. In fact, we can obtain from this example the criterion we shall use for deciding when two fractions belong to the same family. Notice that $\frac{6}{2}$ and $\frac{9}{3}$, which belong to the same family, have the property that the numerator of each times the denominator of the other gives the same product, that is, $6 \cdot 3 = 9 \cdot 2$.

We are now ready to start building up the new number system. First, we take all possible ordered pairs of integers, such as 6 and 2, 5 and 7, -2 and 3, or -3 and -9, in which the second number in the pair is not zero. Then we write the "quotients" of the numbers in the pair, using the first number as numerator. So we now have a collection of fractions or quotients like $\frac{6}{2}, \frac{5}{7}, \frac{-2}{3}$, and $\frac{-3}{-9}$. Next, we associate

75

with each fraction a family of fractions according to the following rule: The family of fractions belonging to $\frac{a}{b}$, where b is not zero, consists of all those fractions $\frac{u}{v}$ for which $a \cdot v = u \cdot b$. To designate the family, we shall write the fraction $\frac{a}{b}$ inside parentheses. Thus, $\left(\frac{a}{b}\right)$ means the family of fractions belonging to $\frac{a}{b}$. We call such a family of fractions a *rational number*.

The rational numbers have some properties analogous to those of integers. First, a fraction belongs to its own family. Secondly, if one of two fractions belongs to the family of the other, then they have the same family. Because of these properties, each fraction belongs to one and only one rational number. A rational number can be represented by putting on display inside parentheses any one of the fractions that belongs to it. For example, since $\frac{9}{3}$ belongs to the rational number $\left(\frac{6}{2}\right)$, $\left(\frac{6}{2}\right) = \left(\frac{9}{3}\right)$. Finally, the criterion for membership in a rational number also serves as a test for equality of rational numbers. That is, the rational numbers $\left(\frac{a}{b}\right)$ and $\left(\frac{c}{d}\right)$ are equal if and only if $a \cdot d = c \cdot b$. For example, we know that $\left(\frac{6}{2}\right) = \left(\frac{9}{3}\right)$ because $6 \cdot 3 = 9 \cdot 2$.

Addition and Multiplication of Rational Numbers

Addition and multiplication of rational numbers are defined by the following equations:

$$\left(\frac{a}{b}\right) + \left(\frac{c}{d}\right) = \left(\frac{a \cdot d + b \cdot c}{b \cdot d}\right)$$

$$\left(\frac{a}{b}\right) \cdot \left(\frac{c}{d}\right) = \left(\frac{a \cdot c}{b \cdot d}\right)$$

For example, $\left(\frac{2}{3}\right) + \left(\frac{3}{5}\right) = \left(\frac{2 \cdot 5 + 3 \cdot 3}{3 \cdot 5}\right) = \left(\frac{19}{15}\right)$,

and $\left(\frac{2}{3}\right) \cdot \left(\frac{3}{5}\right) = \left(\frac{2 \cdot 3}{3 \cdot 5}\right) = \left(\frac{6}{15}\right)$.

To carry out the addition or multiplication of rational numbers, we apply these definitions to whatever fractions are on display inside the parentheses to represent the rational numbers. Since each rational number may be represented by any one of its members, the addition or multiplication may be carried out in many ways. The definitions make sense only if the result comes out the same no matter which member of a rational number is used to represent it. This turns out to be so. For example, we just obtained as the sum of $\left(\frac{2}{3}\right)$ and $\left(\frac{3}{5}\right)$ the rational number $\left(\frac{19}{15}\right)$. But $\left(\frac{2}{3}\right) = \left(\frac{4}{6}\right)$, since $2 \cdot 6 = 4 \cdot 3$; and $\left(\frac{3}{5}\right) = \left(\frac{12}{20}\right)$, since $3 \cdot 20 = 12 \cdot 5$. So we can add $\left(\frac{2}{3}\right)$ and $\left(\frac{3}{5}\right)$ by applying the definition to $\left(\frac{4}{6}\right)$ and $\left(\frac{12}{20}\right)$. We get the sum $\left(\frac{4 \cdot 20 + 6 \cdot 12}{6 \cdot 20}\right) = \left(\frac{152}{120}\right)$. But this is the same answer we got before, because $152 \cdot 15 = 19 \cdot 120$, showing that $\left(\frac{152}{120}\right) = \left(\frac{19}{15}\right)$.

With addition and multiplication defined in this way, the rational numbers form a number system, because they obey the five laws. We prove this fact here only for the commutative law of addition:

$$\left(\frac{a}{b}\right) + \left(\frac{c}{d}\right) = \left(\frac{a \cdot d + b \cdot c}{b \cdot d}\right)$$

$$\left(\frac{c}{d}\right) + \left(\frac{a}{b}\right) = \left(\frac{c \cdot b + d \cdot a}{d \cdot b}\right)$$

But the a, b, c, and d appearing in these symbols are integers, and integers obey the commutative laws for addition and multiplication. Therefore $b \cdot d = d \cdot b$, showing that the two results have the same denominator; and $a \cdot d + b \cdot c = c \cdot b + d \cdot a$, showing that the two results have the same numerator. Therefore the two sums are the same and $\left(\frac{a}{b}\right) + \left(\frac{c}{d}\right) = \left(\frac{c}{d}\right) + \left(\frac{a}{b}\right)$. A similar proof can be given for each of the other four laws.

Zero, Unity and Negatives

Like the natural number system and the system of integers, the rational number system has a zero element and a unity element. The rational number $\left(\frac{0}{1}\right)$ is the zero element, because $\left(\frac{0}{1}\right) + \left(\frac{x}{y}\right) = \left(\frac{0 \cdot y + 1 \cdot x}{1 \cdot y}\right) = \left(\frac{0 + x}{y}\right) = \left(\frac{x}{y}\right)$. The zero element can also be written in the form $\left(\frac{0}{b}\right)$, where b is any integer different from zero. This is proved by the test for equality of rational numbers, because $0 \cdot 1 = 0 \cdot b$. Where there is no danger of confusion with the zero of the system of integers, we use the symbol 0 for the zero element of the rational numbers, too.

The rational number $\left(\frac{1}{1}\right)$ is the unity element, because $\left(\frac{1}{1}\right) \cdot \left(\frac{x}{y}\right) = \left(\frac{1 \cdot x}{1 \cdot y}\right) = \left(\frac{x}{y}\right)$. The unity element can also be written in the form $\left(\frac{b}{b}\right)$, where b is any integer different from zero. This is proved by the fact that $1 \cdot b = b \cdot 1$. So $\left(\frac{2}{2}\right)$, $\left(\frac{3}{3}\right)$, $\left(\frac{4}{4}\right)$, and $\left(\frac{-5}{-5}\right)$ are all legitimate ways of representing the unity element. A rational number is the unity element if it is represented by a fraction whose numerator and denominator are equal. Where there is no danger of confusion with the unity element of the system of integers, we let the symbol 1 stand for the unity element of the rational numbers, too.

The system of integers has one important property that the natural number system does not have: every number in the system has a negative. The system of rational numbers has this property, too. In fact, if $\left(\dfrac{a}{b}\right)$ is any rational number, then $\left(\dfrac{-a}{b}\right)$ is its negative. To prove this fact, we must show that their sum is the zero element:

$\left(\dfrac{a}{b}\right) + \left(\dfrac{-a}{b}\right) = \left(\dfrac{a \cdot b + b \cdot (-a)}{b \cdot b}\right)$. The numerator of the fraction on display for the sum is $a \cdot b + b \cdot (-a)$. By the commutative law for multiplication of integers, $a \cdot b$ can be replaced by $b \cdot a$, so the numerator is equal to $b \cdot a + b \cdot (-a)$. By the distributive law for integers, this sum is equal to $b \cdot (a + (-a))$. But $a + (-a) = 0$, so we finally have that the numerator is equal to $b \cdot 0 = 0$. Therefore $\left(\dfrac{a}{b}\right) + \left(\dfrac{-a}{b}\right) = \left(\dfrac{0}{b \cdot b}\right)$ the zero element in the rational number system.

The Reciprocal of a Rational Number

The negative of a number was defined in terms of addition: one number is the negative of another if the sum of the two numbers is zero. The analogous concept in relation to multiplication is that of the *reciprocal*. One number is called the reciprocal of another if the product of the two numbers is the unity element. In the natural number system, 1 is the only number that has a reciprocal. In fact, it is its own reciprocal, since $1 \cdot 1 = 1$. In the system of integers, there are only two numbers that have reciprocals. They are 1 and -1. Each of them is its own reciprocal, because $1 \cdot 1 = 1$, and $(-1) \cdot (-1) = 1$. But in the rational number system, the existence of reciprocals becomes the rule rather than the exception. *Every rational number except the zero element in that system has a reciprocal. In fact, if $\left(\dfrac{a}{b}\right)$*

is any rational number that is not the zero element, then a is not 0. Consequently, $\left(\dfrac{b}{a}\right)$ is also a rational number, and it is the reciprocal of $\left(\dfrac{a}{b}\right)$. To prove that it is, we multiply them. The product $\left(\dfrac{a}{b}\right) \cdot \left(\dfrac{b}{a}\right) = \left(\dfrac{a \cdot b}{b \cdot a}\right) =$ the unity element, since the numerator and the denominator of the fraction on display are equal.

Since every rational number except the zero element has a reciprocal, it is convenient to introduce a special symbol to mean "the reciprocal of." If A stands for any rational number that is different from zero, we write $\dfrac{1}{A}$ for the reciprocal of A. Then, by the definition of reciprocal, we know that $A \cdot \dfrac{1}{A} = \dfrac{1}{A} \cdot A = 1$.

We undertook the construction of the system of rational numbers for the purpose of finding a number system in which the equation $B \cdot X = A$ always has a solution, as long as B is not zero. We can now show that we have achieved our purpose. If B and A are rational numbers, and B is not zero, then B has a reciprocal, $\dfrac{1}{B}$. If we multiply both sides of the equation by $\dfrac{1}{B}$ we get $\dfrac{1}{B} \cdot B \cdot X = \dfrac{1}{B} \cdot A$. But $\dfrac{1}{B} \cdot B = 1$, so we have $1 \cdot X = \dfrac{1}{B} \cdot A$. But $1 \cdot X = X$, because of the characteristic property of a unity element. Therefore we have found a solution to the equation. In fact, we know that X must be equal to $\dfrac{1}{B} \cdot A$. Since solving the equation $B \cdot X = A$ is another way of saying divide A by B, our result suggests a definition of division that is appropriate for rational numbers. To *divide* by a rational number means to multiply by its reciprocal. In the system of rational numbers, division is always possible as long as the divisor is different from 0.

We Still Have the Integers

By constructing the rational number system, we have gained something, in that every number in it except 0 has a reciprocal. At the same time, we have lost nothing, because we still have the original system of integers hidden within the rational number system in disguise. That is, there is a subset of the rational number system that is isomorphic to the system of integers, and therefore can take its place for all practical purposes. This subset consists of all rational numbers of the form $\left(\dfrac{a}{1}\right)$, where a is any integer, positive, negative, or 0. In fact, suppose we set up a mapping which matches each integer a with the rational number $\left(\dfrac{a}{1}\right)$. This mapping turns out to be an isomorphism, because, under this mapping, the image of a product is the product of the images, and the image of a sum is the sum of the images. The proof of this fact is seen in the following equations obtained by merely applying the definitions of addition and multiplication of rational numbers to the numbers $\left(\dfrac{a}{1}\right)$ and $\left(\dfrac{b}{1}\right)$:

$$\left(\frac{a}{1}\right) + \left(\frac{b}{1}\right) = \left(\frac{a \cdot 1 + 1 \cdot b}{1 \cdot 1}\right) = \left(\frac{a + b}{1}\right)$$

$$\left(\frac{a}{1}\right) \cdot \left(\frac{b}{1}\right) = \left(\frac{a \cdot b}{1 \cdot 1}\right) = \left(\frac{a \cdot b}{1}\right).$$

Because of this isomorphism, the rational number $\left(\dfrac{a}{1}\right)$ may be thought of as being the "same" as the integer a, and we use the symbol for the integer as an abbreviated notation for the corresponding rational number. So, from now on, we shall write 0 instead of $\left(\dfrac{0}{1}\right)$, and 1 instead of $\left(\dfrac{1}{1}\right)$, as already agreed. But we shall also write 2 instead of $\left(\dfrac{2}{1}\right)$, -2 instead of $\left(\dfrac{-2}{1}\right)$, and so on. We shall also drop the parentheses in writing a rational number, so that, when we write the fraction $\dfrac{1}{3}$, we shall mean the whole family of fractions of which $\dfrac{1}{3}$ is only a representative. With these conventions, we have the familiar notation for rational numbers that is used in everyday life. A rational number is called *positive* if it can be written as a fraction with positive numerator and denominator. It is called *negative*, if, when its denominator is positive, its numerator is negative.

The Rational Points on a Line

On page 29, we saw how we could represent the natural numbers as points on a line, spaced at equal intervals on one side of the point called 0. This procedure assigned numbers to only some of the points on the line. On page 54, we saw that we could represent the integers as points on a line, too. We equated the positive integers with the natural numbers already associated with points on one side of the 0. Then we placed the negative integers on the other side of the 0. In this way we assigned numbers to more of the points on the line. Now we can continue the process and assign numbers to many of the points that lie between those that represent the integers.

There is a point that divides the distance between 0 and 1 into two equal parts. We call that point $\dfrac{1}{2}$. There are two points that divide the distance between 0 and 1 into three equal parts. We call those points $\dfrac{1}{3}$ and $\dfrac{2}{3}$. By a similar procedure, we can put $-\dfrac{1}{2}$, $-\dfrac{1}{3}$, and $-\dfrac{2}{3}$ between 0 and -1.

This process can be extended so that we can find a point on the line for every rational number, positive or negative. The arrangement on the line makes it possible to talk about larger or smaller rational numbers in the same way that we could talk about larger or smaller integers. Of any two distinct rational numbers, the one that is further to the right is the larger one. Or, as in the case of integers, we can define the meaning of "larger" in this way: If a and b are rational numbers, a is larger than b if $a - b$ is positive.

The rational numbers are quite densely distributed over the whole line. Between any two points that represent rational numbers, there is at least another one that also represents a rational number. In fact, if a and b are two rational numbers, their average, $\dfrac{a + b}{2}$, is also a rational number, and lies between them. The fact that we can always find "in between" numbers makes the rational number system the appropriate one to use to represent measurements where subdivisions of the unit may be needed. By using as many "in between" numbers as we wish, we can refine a scale of measurement as much as we like, and make measurements as precise as the physical limitations of our equipment and our senses will allow us to.

Since the rational numbers are distributed densely over the line, we may guess that we now have a number assigned to every point on the line. But this guess turns out to be false, as we shall see. In fact, the lack of numbers for some points on the line is the next defect in the number system that we shall try to eliminate by expanding it once more.

The Rational Numbers Form a Field

The rational number system, like the system of integers, is an example of a group structure and a ring structure.

Addition of rational numbers is associative. There is an identity element for addition (the zero), and each element has an inverse with respect to addition (the negative). So the rational number system meets all the requirements for being a group with respect to addition. In fact, since addition of rational numbers is commutative, it is an abelian group, and we are conforming to custom by using a plus sign for the group operation. The operation of multiplication in the rational number system is associative, and it is also distributive with respect to addition. With these further properties, the rational number system meets the requirements for being a ring. In fact, since multiplication is commutative, it is a commutative ring. Moreover, it contains a unity element.

In the transition from integers to rational numbers, something new has been added. Every rational number except 0 has a reciprocal. But a reciprocal is simply an inverse with respect to the operation of multiplication. So the rational number system with zero omitted meets all the requirements for being a group with respect to multiplication. It therefore has a double group structure, one for addition, and one for multiplication. A system of this kind, that has a double group structure, is called a *field*. A field is defined as a ring in which a unity element exists, and which has a reciprocal for every element except zero. The presence of these reciprocals makes it possible to carry out division by any element except zero.

The way in which groups, rings, and fields differ from each other may be expressed briefly, though crudely, as follows: A group is a system in which we can perform addition and subtraction. A ring is a system in which we can perform addition, subtraction, and multiplication. A field is a system in which we can perform addition, subtraction, multiplication, and division, except that division by 0 is excluded.

Finite Fields

The rational number system is a field that contains an infinite number of elements. There are also fields that have only a finite number of elements. In fact, we have already encountered some in earlier sections of this book. In the last chapter, we found that the system of residue classes of integers modulo 3 has a ring structure. The elements in the ring are classes called 0, 1, and 2. The multiplication table in this ring is as follows:

·	0	1	2
0	0	0	0
1	0	1	2
2	0	2	1

We see from this table that every element in the ring except zero has a reciprocal. In fact, the reciprocal of 1 is 1, because $1 \cdot 1 = 1$; and the reciprocal of 2 is 2, because $2 \cdot 2 = 1$. So the system of residue classes of integers modulo 3 is a field.

If you did exercise 5 in the "Do It Yourself" section at the end of Chapter III, you have met another finite field. The residue classes of integers modulo 5 constitute a ring with this multiplication table:

·	0	1	2	3	4
0	0	0	0	0	0
1	0	1	2	3	4
2	0	2	4	1	3
3	0	3	1	4	2
4	0	4	3	2	1

This table shows that every element except zero in this system has a reciprocal. In fact, the reciprocal of 1 is 1; the reciprocal of 2 is 3; the reciprocal of 3 is 2; and the reciprocal of 4 is 4.

On the other hand, the residue classes of integers modulo

6 constitute a ring that is *not* a field. The multiplication table for this system, printed on page 68, shows that some of its elements which are not zero do not have a reciprocal. In fact, there is no element whose product with 2, 3, or 4 is equal to 1. So the elements 2, 3, and 4 in this system do not have reciprocals. The reason for this failure is that the number 6 has positive integer divisors besides itself and the number 1. These divisors are 2 and 3. Any integer which is also divisible by 2 or 3 belongs to a residue class that cannot have a reciprocal. Let us prove this fact for an integer divisible by 2.

Suppose that such an integer belongs to residue class a, and we multiply by any other residue class x. We shall show that the product $a \cdot x$ cannot be equal to 1, and so a cannot have a reciprocal. To identify the product of a and x, we follow the directions given on page 65. We pick any member of a and any member of x, multiply them, and then identify the residue class of the product. Identifying the residue class of the product means finding its remainder when it is divided by 6. As the representative of a let us use the member that we know is in it that is divisible by 2. Since it is divisible by 2 we may represent it as $2 \cdot m$, where m is some other integer. Let us designate by k the member we select from class x. Then the product of the two representatives of their classes is $2 \cdot m \cdot k$. Now we divide this product by 6, and obtain a quotient and a remainder, both of which are integers. Let us call the quotient q, and the remainder r. Then, from the fact that a dividend is equal to the divisor times the quotient plus the remainder, we can say that $2 \cdot m \cdot k = 6 \cdot q + r$. Therefore $r = 2 \cdot m \cdot k - 6 \cdot q$. By the distributive law, $r = 2 \cdot (m \cdot k - 3 \cdot q)$. That is, the remainder is divisible by 2. Therefore it cannot be 1. Therefore the residue class to which $2 \cdot m \cdot k$ belongs is not class 1. Therefore the product of class a and class x cannot be class 1, no matter what class x may be.

By means of a similar proof, it can be shown that, in general, the ring of residue classes modulo n is not a field if n has positive integer divisors besides itself and the number

86

1. An integer that has positive integer divisors other than itself and 1 is called *factorable*. An integer that is not factorable is called prime. It can also be shown that if n *is* a prime integer, the ring of residue classes modulo n *is* a field. The integers 3 and 5 are both prime. That is why the ring of residue classes modulo 3 and the ring of residue classes modulo 5 both turned out to be fields.

No Zero Divisors

In the system of integers, we found that the cancellation law for multiplication was a consequence of the fact that the ring of integers has no zero divisors. Since this law is a great convenience in solving equations, it would be useful if it turned out to be true in the rational number system, too. Fortunately, it does, because the rational number system is a field, and *a field cannot have zero divisors*. The proof of this fact flows directly from the definition of zero divisors and the definition of a field. If a field did have zero divisors, there would be two elements in the field, say a and b, both not zero, but whose product is zero. So we could write $a \cdot b = 0$. Since a is not zero, and the system is a field, it has a reciprocal, $\frac{1}{a}$. Multiplying both sides by $\frac{1}{a}$, we get $\frac{1}{a} \cdot a \cdot b = \frac{1}{a} \cdot 0$. But $\frac{1}{a} \cdot a = 1$, and $\frac{1}{a} \cdot 0 = 0$, so we have $1 \cdot b = 0$, or $b = 0$, contradicting the assumption that a and b are both not zero. Therefore it is impossible for a field to have zero divisors.

Ideals in a Field

The special properties of a field also impose some restrictions on the ideals that it may contain. To get acquainted with these restrictions, let us first recall the definition of an ideal, and note some facts about the ideals of rings in general. We defined an ideal as a subring of a ring that has the property that if we multiply any member of the subring by any member of the ring, whether it is in the subring or not, the product turns out to be in the subring. For example, the set of all *even* integers is an ideal in the ring of integers because, first, it is a subring, and secondly, the product of an even integer and *any* integer is an even integer.

Every ring contains at least two ideals. One of them is the subset consisting of only one element, the 0 of the ring. The other is the entire ring itself.

To show that the subset that contains only the 0 element is an ideal, we check to see if it fits the definition of an ideal. Notice first that addition within this subset is associative and commutative because it is in the ring as a whole. Multiplication within the subset is associative, and is distributive with respect to addition because it is in the ring as a whole. We observe next that the subset $\{0\}$ contains the zero element, and also the negative of each of its elements, since 0 is its own negative. Moreover, $0 + 0 = 0$, so the sum of elements in the subset is in the subset. Therefore the subset meets all the requirements for being an abelian group. The product $0 \cdot 0 = 0$, and so is a member of the subset. And, since multiplication in it is associative and distributive with respect to addition, the subset meets all the requirements for being a subring. Now we observe that any element in the ring times 0 gives a product equal to 0, so that this product is also in the subring. This last property makes the subring an ideal. Similarly, checking the requirements one by one, we see that the original ring is one of its ideals.

The ideal that consists of the zero element alone is called the *zero ideal*. We shall also assign a special name to the original ring when viewed as one of its own ideals. We call it the *unit ideal*. The reason for this name is seen in the following considerations. Suppose the ring we are talking about has a unity element. (This is not true of all rings, as we saw on page 64, but it is true of all fields.) Let us take a close look at any ideal that contains the unity element 1. The characteristic property of an ideal is that when we multiply a member of the ideal by any member of the ring, the product is a member of the ideal. Let us, then, multiply 1 by any element x in the ring. The product, $x \cdot 1 = x$ is therefore in the ideal. In other words, every element in the ring is in the ideal. So, if an ideal contains the unity element, it contains all the elements of the ring, and therefore must be the whole ring. That is why the ideal that consists of the whole ring is called the unit ideal. We have in this fact and in this name a test for recognizing when an ideal is the unit ideal. To show that an ideal is the unit ideal of a ring, it suffices to show that the ideal contains the element 1.

Since a field is a ring, it has these two special ideals, the zero ideal and the unit ideal. Now we show that a field has no other ideals besides these two. Suppose we examine any ideal of a field. Since the ideal is a subring, it must contain the 0 element. If it contains no other elements, then it is the zero ideal. If it contains some other element, say b, then b is different from zero, and therefore has a reciprocal $\frac{1}{b}$ in the field. If we multiply the element b of the ideal by $\frac{1}{b}$, the product is a member of the ideal. But this product is 1. Therefore the ideal contains 1, and must be the unit ideal. This concludes the proof.

DO IT YOURSELF

1. Separate all integers into residue classes modulo 7, by putting into one class all the integers that have the same remainder when you divide by 7. By using the remainder as the name for the class associated with it, we get seven classes called 0, 1, 2, 3, 4, 5, and 6. Construct the multiplication table for these residue classes (see page 65). Verify from the table that each element in this system except 0 has a reciprocal. What are the reciprocals of 2, 3, 4, 5, and 6 in this system?

2. Construct the multiplication table for residue classes modulo 12. Which elements are zero divisors in this system?

CHAPTER V

Filling Out the Line

More Questions to Be Answered

SO FAR we have expanded the number system twice, from natural numbers to integers, and then from integers to rational numbers. In each case, the purpose of the expansion was to have a number system in which a certain type of equation would always have a solution. The first type of equation we tried to solve was one that included only a single step of addition. This was the equation of the form $b + x = a$. The second type of equation we tried to solve included only a single step of multiplication. This was the equation of the form $b \cdot x = a$. It was natural to consider these equations first, because addition and multiplication are the operations that are built into the structure of a number system.

It is just as natural now to go beyond these simplest equations, and consider others that may include *both* operations, or may use an operation *more than once*. For example, we might examine equations like $2 \cdot x + 5 = 11$, or $3 \cdot (x + 2) = 7$ which involve both addition and multiplication. We could also consider an equation like $3 \cdot x \cdot x \cdot x -5 \cdot x \cdot x = 2 \cdot x + 9$ where the operation of multiplication is repeated several times. Such equations, in which only addition and multiplication may be employed, are known as *algebraic equations*.

For a systematic survey of these equations, we first re-write them in standard form. Wherever the unknown "x" is multiplied by itself several times, we use the abbreviated power notation, writing x^2 for $x \cdot x$, x^3 for $x \cdot x \cdot x$, and so on. We eliminate parentheses by using the distributive law.

90

For example, $3 \cdot (x + 2)$ can be replaced by $3 \cdot x + 6$. We reduce one side of the equation to 0 by adding negatives where necessary. For example, in the equation $x^2 - 3x = x + 6$, if we add $-x - 6$ to both sides of the equation, we get $x^2 - 3x - x - 6 = 0$. Finally, we combine like terms, and arrange all terms in descending powers of x, getting $x^2 - 4x - 6 = 0$.

Here are some typical equations, written in standard form, using numbers that belong to the rational number system:

$$\frac{2}{3} \cdot x - \frac{5}{2} = 0.$$

$$\frac{3}{7} \cdot x^2 + \frac{5}{3} \cdot x - \frac{1}{2} = 0$$

$$x^3 - 2 \cdot x^2 + \frac{1}{3} \cdot x - 5 = 0$$

The highest power of x that appears in an algebraic equation in standard form is called the *degree* of the equation. *In the rational number system, an equation of the first degree always has a solution.* The typical first degree equation has the form $a \cdot x + b = 0$, where a and b are rational numbers, and a is different from 0. To solve it, we take advantage of the fact that every rational number has a negative, and every rational number that is different from 0 has a reciprocal. First we add to both sides of the equation the number $-b$, which is the negative of b. This gives us $a \cdot x = -b$. Then we multiply both sides of the equation by $\frac{1}{a}$, which is the reciprocal of a, and we find that $x = \frac{1}{a} \cdot (-b)$. This result tells us that if there is a solution to the equation, it must be equal to $\frac{1}{a}(-b)$. We verify that it is indeed a solution by substituting into the equation. For example, to solve the equation $\frac{2}{3} \cdot x - \frac{5}{2} = 0$, first add $\frac{5}{2}$ to both sides of the equation. Then multiply both sides by $\frac{3}{2}$. The result asserts that if there is a solution, it must be equal to $\frac{3}{2} \cdot \frac{5}{2}$, or $\frac{15}{4}$. If we substitute $\frac{15}{4}$ for x in the equation, it then says $\frac{2}{3} \cdot \frac{15}{4} - \frac{5}{2} = 0$. Calculation shows that this statement is true, so that $\frac{15}{4}$ really is a solution to the equation.

However, we have less luck when we try to solve equations of the second degree. In the rational number system, we can solve some of them, but we cannot solve others. For example, we can solve without any difficulty the equation $x^2 - 1 = 0$. First add 1 to both sides and we get $x^2 = 1$. In this form, the equation asks, "What number, when multiplied by itself, gives 1 as the product?" The number 1 is obviously an answer to this question, because $1 \cdot 1 = 1$. In fact, the number -1 is also a good answer to the question, because $(-1) \cdot (-1) = 1$. So we have found two solutions to the equation. The equation $x^2 - 2 = 0$ looks as though it ought to be just as easy to solve, but it isn't. If we add 2 to both sides, we get $x^2 = 2$. In this form, the equation asks, "What number, when multiplied by itself, gives 2 as the product?" We may be tempted to say that the answer is $\sqrt{2}$, or the square root of 2. But this is really not an answer to the question. It is only a restatement of the question. When we write the symbol $\sqrt{2}$, it signifies, "that number (if it exists) which when multiplied by itself gives 2 as the product." But the question still remains, "Does it exist?" We shall soon see that it does not exist in the rational number system. We shall prove that there is no rational number whose square is equal to 2.

Before giving the proof, let us approach the question in another way. We find that the question we are trying to answer is one that comes up in a simple problem in geometry. Suppose we construct a square whose sides are one unit long, and then draw the diagonal of the square. The diagonal has a definite length. To calculate it, we use the Pythagorean

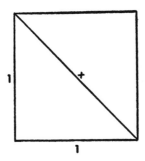

theorem that states that the square of the hypotenuse of a right triangle is equal to the sum of the squares of the legs. In this case the theorem leads to the equation $x^2 = 1^2 + 1^2$, or $x^2 = 2$, which is precisely the equation that we are trying to solve. So, when we prove that there is no rational number whose square is equal to 2, we shall be proving at the same time that no rational number can represent the length of the diagonal of a square whose side has length 1.

The proof makes use of some simple facts about rational numbers and integers that we shall take note of first. 1) Every rational number can be represented by a fraction that is "reduced to lowest terms." 2) If a fraction is reduced to lowest terms, then its numerator and denominator cannot both be even numbers. For, if they were, it would mean that the fraction can be reduced further by dividing numerator and denominator by 2. For example, $\frac{6}{8}$ is not in lowest terms. It can be reduced to $\frac{3}{4}$. 3) The square of an even integer is an even integer, and the square of an odd integer is an odd integer. For example, $6 \cdot 6 = 36$, which is an even integer; $7 \cdot 7 = 49$, which is an odd integer. From this fact, it follows that if the square of an integer is even, then the integer itself is even.

We prove that there is no rational number whose square is equal to 2 by showing that the assumption that there is one leads to a contradiction. Suppose there is a rational number whose square is equal to 2. Then it can be represented by a fraction that is reduced to lowest terms. Let $\frac{a}{b}$ represent this fraction, where a and b are both integers. Since the fraction is in lowest terms, *a and b are not both even integers*. Since the square of this fraction is supposed to be equal to 2, we can write $\frac{a^2}{b^2} = 2$. Multiplying both sides by b^2, we find that $a^2 = 2 \cdot b^2$. This equation tells us that a^2 is double the integer b^2, so a^2 is an even integer. But if a^2 is even, then a must be even, that is, it is double some other integer. If we call that other integer k, then $a = 2 \cdot k$. In that case, $a^2 = (2 \cdot k)(2 \cdot k) = 4 \cdot k^2$. If we substitute this expression for a^2 in the equation $a^2 = 2 \cdot b^2$, we get $4 \cdot k^2 = 2 \cdot b^2$. Dividing both sides by 2, we see that $2 \cdot k^2 = b^2$. In other words, b^2 is double the integer k^2, or b^2 is an even integer. But if b^2 is even, *then b must be even*. We began by observing that a and b are not both even, and end up by concluding that they are both even. We were led to this contradiction by the assumption that there is a rational number whose square is equal to 2. Therefore we are compelled to reject the assumption.

The proof given above is a very old one. It was first worked out about 2500 years ago by the Greek mathematician Pythagoras. The philosophers of Greece were so pleased to discover that there were lengths that could not be represented by rational numbers, that they celebrated the discovery, we are told, by sacrificing one hundred oxen to the gods.

In Chapter IV we represented the rational numbers as points on a line. In this representation, wherever a positive number is attached to a point, the number represents the distance of that point from 0, if we use the distance from 0 to 1 as the unit of length. Suppose, now, we measure out to the right of 0 a length equal to the length of the diagonal of a square whose side has length 1 (see diagram on page 102). In this way we locate a definite point whose distance from 0 is equal to the length of the diagonal. But we have just proved that there is no rational number that can represent this length. So we have found a point on the line that has no rational number attached to it. This discovery answers the question that we raised on page 83. The rational number system supplies numbers for some, but not all, of the points on the line. Even though the rational numbers are spread out densely over the line, there are gaps that they leave unfilled. If we want to have a number to represent every point on the line, we have to expand the number system again. We proceed to do so now, in order to fill the gaps.

Decimal Fractions

There are many ways of approaching the problem of filling the gaps between the rational numbers. We shall use here an approach that grows naturally out of the custom of writing numbers as "decimals." Decimals are more correctly described as decimal fractions. The decimal .2 is an abbreviated way of writing the fraction $\frac{2}{10}$. The decimal .23 is an abbreviated way of writing the fraction $\frac{23}{100}$. In each case, the denominator is understood to be a power of 10, and we identify the power by counting the number of digits to the right of the decimal point. Thus, since .235 has three digits after the decimal point, we know the denominator is 10^3 or 1000, and the decimal .235 represents the fraction $\frac{235}{1000}$. So we see that each decimal represents a fraction, and therefore is simply another way of writing some of the numbers in the rational number system. This observation immediately suggests the question, "Can every rational number be written as a decimal?" We are led to a rather interesting problem when we try to answer this question.

In elementary school we learned that we can convert a fraction into a decimal by using the process of long division. For example, to get the decimal equivalent of $\frac{1}{4}$, we divide 4 into 1, using the following form:

$$
\begin{array}{r}
.25 \\
4\overline{\smash{\big)}\,1.00} \\
\underline{8} \\
20 \\
\underline{20}
\end{array}
$$

The long division terminates after two steps because in the last subtraction the remainder is zero. The conclusion is that $\frac{1}{4}$ = .25. If we try the same procedure to get a decimal equivalent for the fraction $\frac{1}{3}$, we run into trouble. We arrange the work in the same way, as follows:

$$
\begin{array}{r}
.3333 \\
3\overline{\smash{\big)}\,1.0000} \\
\underline{9} \\
10 \\
\underline{9} \\
10 \\
\underline{9} \\
10 \\
\underline{9} \\
1
\end{array}
$$

But, no matter how many steps we carry out, the division never comes to an end. After each subtraction there is a remainder of 1. So the fraction $\frac{1}{3}$ cannot be represented as a decimal with a finite number of digits.

The persistent reappearance of the remainder 1 tempts us to keep dividing. If we do so, we get a decimal that never ends. If we want to represent the fraction $\frac{1}{3}$ by a decimal at all, it will have to be an *infinite decimal*, that is, one that has an infinite number of digits after the decimal point. So, to decide whether every rational number can be represented as a decimal we have to investigate what meaning, if any, an infinite decimal can have.

To interpret the meaning of a finite decimal, we identify a numerator from the digits that we see, and a denominator by using the appropriate power of ten, indicated by the number of digits that appear after the decimal point. Then we put the two together in the form of a fraction. This method breaks down with an infinite decimal, so we have to try another approach. What we do is think of the infinite decimal as a sequence of finite decimals, made progressively longer by appending another digit at each step. In this view, the infinite decimal .333333 . . . . represents the infinite sequence of finite decimals .3, .33, .333, .3333, .33333, ... To see how this sequence is related to the fraction $\frac{1}{3}$, let us compare each of the numbers in the sequence with the fraction. Suppose, for example, we subtract .3 from $\frac{1}{3}$. Writing the decimal as a common fraction, we say $\frac{1}{3} - \frac{3}{10} = \frac{10}{30} - \frac{9}{30} = \frac{1}{30}$. This difference is rather small, and in many practical problems is small enough to be considered negligible. So we may use .3 as an approximation of the value of $\frac{1}{3}$. If we subtract .33 from $\frac{1}{3}$, we find the difference to be $\frac{1}{300}$. This difference is smaller than $\frac{1}{30}$, so .33 is a better approximation to the value of $\frac{1}{3}$ than .3 is. If we try each of the decimals in the sequence in turn, we get better and better approximations to the number $\frac{1}{3}$. The longer the decimal is, the better the approximation becomes, because the difference from $\frac{1}{3}$ gets smaller and smaller. To approximate means

97

literally to come close. By taking more and more digits in the decimal we get a number that is closer and closer to $\frac{1}{3}$.

In fact, we can get as close to $\frac{1}{3}$ as we please by simply taking a decimal that is long enough. We describe the situation by saying that the sequence of decimals approaches the number $\frac{1}{3}$ as a limit.

We now have the means of explaining how an infinite decimal may represent a number. An infinite decimal represents a number if the sequence of finite decimals obtained by taking more and more of its digits approaches that number as a limit. With this definition of the meaning of an infinite decimal, it may make as much sense as a finite decimal, and we can now answer the question, "Can every rational number be represented by a decimal?" The answer is, "Yes, by a finite or infinite decimal."

A Nest of Intervals

The meaning of an infinite decimal can also be expressed pictorially in terms of our representation of the rational numbers as points on a line. It can be interpreted as a description of the position of a number, or directions that may be followed in order to find it.

Suppose, for example, we want to describe where the number $\frac{1}{3}$ is located. Since it is a rational number, we can say first that it is somewhere on the line on which the rational numbers are represented. Then we try to specify where it is on the line. The integers on the line divide the line into intervals of unit length. We can assign a name to each interval by using the number that is attached to the end that is nearest to 0. We call the interval between 0 and 1 the "0 interval"; the interval between 1 and 2 the "1 interval," and so on. On the negative side of the line, we call the interval between 0 and -1 the "-0 interval," the interval between -1 and -2, the "-1 interval." Notice that 0 and -0 refer to different intervals.

Now we can be more specific about where the number $\frac{1}{3}$ is by saying that it is in the 0 interval. So we write down 0 as the first part of a chain of directions. The next step in the description is to say where it is in the 0 interval. For this purpose, we divide the 0 interval into ten equal parts, each with length .1. We label these intervals in order, starting with the one nearest to the 0, as 0.0, 0.1, 0.2, 0.3, 0.4, 0.5, 0.6, 0.7, 0.8, and 0.9. Now we learn from long division that $\frac{1}{3}$ is more than 0.3, but less than 0.4, so it lies in the interval whose name is 0.3. The name of this interval incorporates both parts of the description we have given so far. It tells us that the number $\frac{1}{3}$ is in the 0 interval, and that within

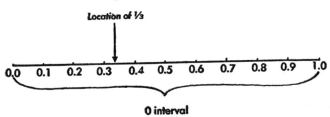

that interval it is in the sub-interval that has 0.3 as its left end. Now we narrow down its location once more. We divide the sub-interval into ten equal parts, each of width .01, and label them, in order, 0.30, 0.31, 0.32, 0.33, 0.34, 0.35, 0.36, 0.37, 0.38, and 0.39. Again we learn from long division that $\frac{1}{3}$ is more than 0.33, but less than 0.34. So it lies in the interval whose name is 0.33. The name of this interval is a three part description. It says that the number $\frac{1}{3}$ is in the 0 interval, and inside this interval it is in the 0.3 interval, and inside the latter interval it is in the 0.33 interval. Now we subdivide this interval, and continue the process indefinitely.

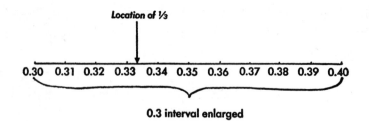

0.30 0.31 0.32 0.33 0.34 0.35 0.36 0.37 0.38 0.39 0.40

0.3 interval enlarged

Each time we pick out the sub-interval that contains the point. According to this scheme, the infinite decimal 0.33333 . . . . represents an infinite sequence of intervals, with the following characteristics: each successive interval lies inside the interval that precedes it in the sequence, and as we move along the sequence, the width of the intervals shrinks toward 0. We call such a sequence of intervals a *nest of intervals*.

In this instance, we chose each interval in the nest as an interval that contains the number $\frac{1}{3}$. So we are sure that the number $\frac{1}{3}$ lies inside every one of the infinite number of intervals in the nest. We can also be sure that no other number can be in there with it, because two different numbers cannot lie in the same nest. This is so, because two different numbers are separated by a distance that is greater than 0. Since the inner intervals in a nest shrink in width toward a width of 0, ultimately the innermost intervals are too narrow to span the distance between two separate points, and cannot enclose them both. For this reason, the nest of intervals represented by the infinite decimal 0.333 . . . . describes the number $\frac{1}{3}$ and no other number. *A nest of intervals represents a number if that number is attached to the only point that lies inside all the intervals of the nest.*

A Nest for Every Rational Number

By following the same procedure with any rational number, we can find a nest of intervals that contains the number, and the nest of intervals can be represented by an infinite decimal. In this way we can get an infinite decimal for every rational number. This is true even for numbers that are represented by finite decimals. In fact, in these cases, the number can be represented by two infinite decimals. Suppose, for example, we look for a nest of intervals and the associated infinite decimal to represent the number 2.3. First we notice that the number lies in the 2 interval which extends from 2 to 3. Now, when we subdivide this interval into ten equal parts, one of the points of division is actually 2.3. As a point of division, it belongs to *two* intervals. It is the right end of the interval whose name is 2.2. It is also the left end of the interval whose name is 2.3. So we may choose either one as the interval to which it belongs. After we have made that choice, we shall not be free to choose again. If we think of the number as belonging to 2.2, then forever after, as we subdivide the intervals, the number will always lie in the last subdivision. The infinite decimal in this case comes out 2.2999999 . . . . with an endless series of nines. If we think of the number as belonging to 2.3, then forever after, as we subdivide the intervals, the number will always lie in the first subdivision. Then the infinite decimal comes out 2.3000000 . . . . with an endless series of zeros. We get two names like this for every number that can be represented as a finite decimal, because a finite decimal turns up, sooner or later, as an endpoint of an interval in the nest. The two different ways of representing the number signify that such a number can be approached from two directions, from the left or from the right.

A Nest That Has No Number

We have answered in the affirmative the question, "Can every rational number be represented by a decimal?" We have found that it can be represented by an infinite decimal, and in some cases by two infinite decimals. In each case the infinite decimal represents a nest of intervals, and the rational number is attached to the only point that is inside the nest.

Now let us reverse the question and ask, "Does every

infinite decimal represent a rational number?" Or, to ask the question in another form, "Does every nest of intervals defined by an infinite decimal have a rational number attached to the point inside the nest?" We can see immediately that the answer to this question is, "No." We found before that there are some points on the line that have no rational number attached. The point whose distance from 0 is equal to the length of the diagonal of a unit square is such a point. Its location is pointed out by the arrow in the diagram. However, we can follow the same procedure with this point as we did with the point that represents the fraction $\frac{1}{3}$. We can locate it precisely by means of a nest of

intervals, and the associated infinite decimal. We observe first from the diagram that the point lies between 1 and 2 so the decimal begins with the number 1. Then we subdivide the interval between 1 and 2, and observe that the point lies between 1.4 and 1.5. In fact, we can verify this fact by arithmetic, by observing that $1.4 \times 1.4 = 1.96$, a number that is less than 2, while $1.5 \times 1.5 = 2.25$, a number that is more than 2. So, 1.4 is too small to be the length of the diagonal of the unit square, and 1.5 is too large. By continuing the process of subdivision, we get a nest of intervals and an infinite decimal that represents it. There is one and only one point inside this nest, the point whose distance from 0 is the length of the diagonal of the unit square. But there is no rational number attached to this point. So the infinite decimal that belongs to this nest does not represent a rational number.

The Real Number System

We can think of an infinite decimal as a question. It asks, "If you make the nest of intervals that my digits describe, what number will you find inside the nest?" In the rational number system this question does not always have an answer. So, once again, we ask, "Is there a larger number system in which such a question does always have an answer?" To construct such a number system, we use the same device we have already used twice before. We make the question its own answer. We build a new number system in which each element *is* an infinite decimal. We call this system the system of *real* numbers. In general, each separate infinite decimal is a separate number. But, we know from our experience with the rational number 2.3 that we shall have to provide for some exceptions. We must specify that whenever a decimal ends with an infinite chain of nines, as 2.99999 . . . does, the decimal obtained by replacing the chain of nines by a chain of zeros and adding 1 to the last digit before the chain will represent the same number. Thus 2.300000 . . . . and 2.299999 . . . . will represent the same number. Under this agreement, every real number is either a single infinite decimal, or a pair of infinite decimals either one of which may be used to represent the pair.

When we represented the rational numbers as points on a line, we found that there were gaps on the line, where no numbers were attached. Later we found that every point on the line can be located by an infinite decimal, and now we are converting every infinite decimal into a number. So, at one stroke, we are filling all the gaps on the line. The real number system gives us a number for every point on the line.

So far we have merely defined a collection of elements, each of which is an infinite decimal or a pair of decimals. To convert this collection into a number system we have to give it the structure that every number system must have. We have to define operations of addition and multiplication on these elements, and we must show that the operations obey the five laws. To define the operations, we lean on the

103

smaller number system we already have as a crutch. Just as we used the natural numbers when we built the structure of the system of integers, and we used the integers when we built the structure of the system of rational numbers, we now use the rational numbers when we build the structure of the system of real numbers. We define addition and multiplication of real numbers as follows:

To add two infinite decimals, break up each decimal into a sequence of finite decimals, by using in succession, more and more of the digits in the decimal. These finite decimals represent rational numbers, and may be added by the rules for rational numbers. So, first add the first numbers in each sequence. The sum is a first approximation to your answer. Then add the second numbers in each sequence. This gives you a better approximation to your answer. As you proceed with the sequence of additions, you get a longer and longer finite decimal. The digits at the beginning of the decimal may fluctuate at first, but then settle down so that ultimately a fixed digit is defined for each decimal place. In this way a specific infinite decimal is obtained as the sum. To multiply infinite decimals, multiply the successive pairs of finite decimals in the same way.

For example, to add 0.2222222 .... and 0.8888888 ...., we proceed by these steps:

0.2	0.22	0.222	0.2222	0.22222	0.222222
+0.8	+0.88	+0.888	+0.8888	+0.88888	+0.888888
1.0	1.10	1.110	1.1110	1.11110	1.111110

The sum is clearly the infinite decimal 1.111111 .... in which all the digits are ones. To multiply these same decimals, we proceed by these steps:

0.2	0.22	0.222	0.2222
×0.8	×0.88	×0.888	×0.8888
0.16	176	1776	17776
	176	1776	17776
	0.1936	1776	17776
		0.197136	17776
			0.19749136

We see that the product begins with 0.197, and more of the digits are fixed when more of the steps are taken.

At each step in the addition or multiplication just defined, we are using rational numbers. The rational numbers obey the five laws. As a result, the five laws are extended to the real numbers as well. For example, $0.2 + 0.8$ and $0.8 + 0.2$ lead to the same sum; $0.22 + 0.88$ and $0.88 + 0.22$ lead to the same sum; etc. So $0.222 \ldots + 0.888 \ldots$ and $0.888 \ldots + 0.222 \ldots$ lead to the same infinite decimal as sum. In other words, real numbers obey the commutative law of addition. The other four laws can be established by a similar argument.

We Still Have the Rational Numbers

We constructed the real number system in such a way that we have a number for every point on the number line. Among the points on the line are those to which we had previously assigned rational numbers. Let us refer to these as the rational points on the line. The real numbers assigned to the rational points form a subset of the real number system that is isomorphic to the rational number system. For all practical purposes, they are the "same" as the rational numbers. The symbol for a rational number is a fraction or a finite decimal. Such a symbol is easier to write and work with than an infinite decimal, so we use the rational number rather than the infinite decimal to represent the real number attached to a rational point. But first we must learn to recognize which of the real numbers belong to the rational points, and are therefore entitled to this simpler representation.

The infinite decimals that represent rational points are those which, after a finite number of digits in the decimal, simply repeat a fixed block of one or more digits over and over again. For example, the following decimals, in which the repeating block has been italicized, all represent rational numbers: $0.3333 \ldots$, $0.121212 \ldots$, $2.3745454545 \ldots$. To prove this fact, we have to show, first, that every rational number, represented by a fraction, can be written as a repeating decimal. Then, vice versa, we must show that every repeating decimal can be written as a fraction.

To show that a fraction can be written as a repeating decimal, recall that we can convert a fraction into a decimal by long division, dividing the denominator into the numerator. In the long division process there is a step involving subtraction, after which we carry down a digit from the dividend. The dividend is an integer with a finite number of digits. So these are soon exhausted. Then we begin carrying down the zeros that appear after the decimal point. Consider what happens after we reach this stage of carrying down only zeros. In the subtraction step there is a remainder that is less than the divisor, and this remainder determines what the next number in the quotient will be. Since the remainders must be less than the divisor, the list of possible remainders is a restricted finite list. But, as we proceed with the division, we get an endless succession of remainders. So we cannot keep getting a different remainder each time. Sooner or later, a remainder that turned up before is repeated, and the division process begins to repeat itself.

To show that every repeating decimal can be written as a fraction, we shall work out one specific example showing how it is done. It will be clear that the method used can be employed with any repeating decimal whatever.

Suppose we find the fraction that represents the repeating decimal 2.7*151515* . . . . We first split this decimal into two parts, 2.7, and .0*151515* . . . ., separating the non-repeating part from the repeating part. The first part is the fraction $\frac{27}{10}$.

Now we find a fraction for the second part. First multiply it by ten, so that the repeating block will begin right after the decimal point. Let us call the result x, and remember that it is ten times as big as the number we are looking for, so after we find x we must divide by ten. x = .151515 . . . . Now multiply both sides of this equation by 100. This has the effect of moving the decimal point two places to the right.

We get $100x = 15.1515 \ldots$, which may also be written as $100x = 15 + .1515 \ldots$ But the decimal in this equation is none other than x all over again. So we may write $100x = 15 + x$. Taking x away from both sides, we find that $99x = 15$. Dividing by 99 on both sides, we find that $x = \frac{15}{99}$ or $\frac{5}{33}$. Now we divide by ten, to find that the second part of our original number is $\frac{5}{330}$. So the infinite decimal $2.7151515 \ldots$ is the sum of $\frac{27}{10}$ and $\frac{5}{330}$. Therefore $2.7151515 \ldots$ represents the rational number $\frac{896}{330}$ or $\frac{448}{165}$. To check the result, divide 165 into 448.

We Still Have a Field

The rational number system has the structure of a field. Enlarging the number system has not destroyed this structure, because the real number system, too, is a field. We can verify that it has the characteristics of a field, one by one. In the first place it is a commutative group with the operation of addition. The zero element in the group is the infinite decimal $0.0000 \ldots$, which we may write briefly as 0, and every infinite decimal has a negative, namely, the infinite decimal written with the same digits in the same order, but having the opposite sign attached. For example, the negative of $.333 \ldots$ is $-.333 \ldots$ It is also a ring, because the multiplication is distributive with respect to addition. The unity element may be written in two ways: $1.00000 \ldots$, or $0.9999 \ldots$ Moreover, every element except 0 has a reciprocal, so the system is a field. To find the reciprocal of an infinite decimal, we can use the successive finite decimals that approximate it, and divide each into the number 1. The quotients we get serve as successive approximations of the reciprocal, and, one by one, we can identify the digits in the decimal that represents it. In special cases we have simplified ways of doing it. For example, to find the

reciprocal of $\sqrt{2}$, we write it first in fraction form as $\dfrac{1}{\sqrt{2}}$.
The value is unchanged if we multiply by $\dfrac{\sqrt{2}}{\sqrt{2}}$, because this
multiplier is equal to 1, or the unity element. But then we
have $\dfrac{\sqrt{2}}{2}$, whose decimal equivalent is easily found by
dividing 2 into the decimal for $\sqrt{2}$. The decimal for $\sqrt{2}$
begins as 1.414 . . ., so the decimal for its reciprocal begins
as .707 . . . .

A Number in Every Nest

The system of real numbers has some special properties
that the rational number system does not have. The most
convenient way of expressing these properties is in terms of
the picture we have set up of numbers as points on a line.
When we represented the rational numbers as points on a
line, we found that there were gaps that it left unfilled. That
is, there were points on the line that had no numbers attached to them. The real number system was deliberately
designed to eliminate this defect. In this system, not only
do we have a point for every number. We also have a number
for every point. There is a one-to-one correspondence between the real number system and the points on the number
line. Because of this correspondence, we may think of the
real numbers as the points on the line, and can describe the
properties of the real number system in terms of relationships of the points on the line.

For example, by making every infinite decimal an element
of the real number system, we assured the fact that there
would be a real number for every such decimal. This property
can also be described in terms of points on the line, as we
have seen: an infinite decimal represents a nest of intervals
on the line, and for every such nest, there is one and only
one point that lies inside every interval of the nest. In this
statement, the nest referred to is a nest associated with an
infinite decimal. The successive intervals in such a nest

have a special length, viz., 1, .1, .01, .001, etc., and their endpoints are always finite decimals. However, it is possible to form nests of intervals of a more general character by removing these restrictions on the lengths of the intervals and the locations of their endpoints. The only requirements for calling a sequence of intervals a nest are that the successive intervals lie one inside the other and that the lengths of the inner intervals shrink toward 0. It can be proved that in the real number system, all *nests* have the same property we have found for nests associated with infinite decimals: There is one and only one point that lies inside every interval of the nest. In this sense, every nest of intervals defines a single real number. Some of the other properties of the real number system that we shall now examine are closely related to this fact.

Infinite Series

Addition is an operation defined on a pair of numbers, so, initially, we can add only two numbers at a time. However, by performing one addition after another, we can extend the operation to include any finite number of numbers. For example, there is no difficulty about finding the sum of these numbers: $1 + 1 + 1 + 1 + 1 + 1$. The sum is, of course, 6. However, if we permit the series of ones to go on indefinitely, in the infinite series $1 + 1 + 1 + 1 + 1 + 1 \ldots$, then we run into trouble. The step by step addition that we can carry out with a finite number of terms doesn't work here, because it never comes to an end. We are left then with the question: Does it make any sense at all to try to add an infinite series of terms? The answer turns out to be that sometimes it does, and sometimes it doesn't. We can get clues to when an infinite series has meaning as a sum by re-examining an infinite series with which we are already familiar, namely, an infinite decimal.

The infinite decimal .3333333 . . . . . . is really an infinite series in disguise. In fact, we may think of it as merely an abbreviated way of writing the infinite series $.3 + .03 + .003 + .0003 + .00003 \ldots$ On page 97 we also interpreted the infinite decimal as a sequence of finite decimals, .3, .33, .333, .3333, ... These finite decimals are the sums we get when we add a finite number of terms in the infinite series, using the first term alone, then the first two terms, then the first three, and so on. We call these sums the partial sums of the series. We found that these partial sums come closer and closer in value to the fraction $\frac{1}{3}$, approaching this value as a limit, so we assigned the value $\frac{1}{3}$ to the infinite decimal. In a similar way, we can assign a meaning to some other examples of infinite series. *If the partial sums of a series come closer and closer, in the long run, to some definite number, approaching this number as a limit, then we can assign this limiting number as the sum of the infinite series.*

For example, let us consider the series, $1 + \frac{1}{2} + \frac{1}{4} + \frac{1}{8} + \frac{1}{16} + \ldots$ in which each term is half the size of the term that it follows. The partial sums are, $1, 1\frac{1}{2}, 1\frac{3}{4}, 1\frac{7}{8}, 1\frac{15}{16}, 1\frac{31}{32}, \ldots$ In this case, the partial sums come closer and closer to the number 2. The first sum differs from 2 by 1. The second sum differs from 2 by $\frac{1}{2}$. The third sum differs from 2 by $\frac{1}{4}$. Successive partial sums differ from 2 by smaller and smaller amounts, and the difference can be made as small as we please if we add up enough terms in the series. So the partial sums approach the number 2 as a limit. We therefore can assign the number 2 as the sum of the series $1 + \frac{1}{2} + \frac{1}{4} + \frac{1}{8} + \frac{1}{16} + \ldots$.

Let us try to use the same procedure with the series $1 + 1 + 1 + 1 + \ldots$ . . . The partial sums for this series form the sequence, $1, 2, 3, 4, 5, 6, \ldots$ In this case, there is no number that the partial sums approach as a limit, because they keep increasing without limit. That is, we can get a partial sum to be larger than any number we wish by simply adding enough terms of the series. Because the partial sums do not approach a limit, we cannot assign any number as the sum of this series. So we see that not every infinite series has meaning as a sum. An infinite series has meaning as a sum only if the partial sums of the series approach a limit.

110

In that case we call the series a convergent series, and the sum of the series is the limit approached by the partial sums.

Now that we know that only some infinite series have meaning as a sum, the next logical question to ask is, "Which ones?" How do we recognize an infinite series that converges? We find that we can recognize some very easily by the fact that they define a nest of intervals. For example, consider the series $1 - \frac{1}{2} + \frac{1}{3} - \frac{1}{4} + \frac{1}{5} - \frac{1}{6} + \ldots$, in which the successive terms decrease toward 0 and the signs alternate between $+$ and $-$. As we form the partial sums, let us locate them as points on the line of real numbers. The first partial sum is the number 1. Because the next term, $-\frac{1}{2}$, is negative, the second partial sum is to the left of the first. Adding the

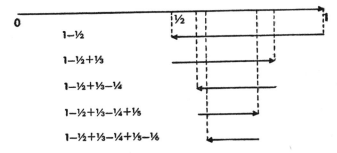

third term, $\frac{1}{3}$, brings us back to the right, but not all the way back, because $\frac{1}{3}$ is smaller than $\frac{1}{2}$. As we add in more and more terms, the point representing the partial sum oscillates back and forth, left and right, but never again as far to the left as before, and never again as far to the right. Now consider the intervals that have successive partial sums as their endpoints. The first interval is bounded on the right by 1 and on the left by $1 - \frac{1}{2}$. The second interval is bounded on the left by $1 - \frac{1}{2}$, and on the right by $1 - \frac{1}{2} + \frac{1}{3}$. The third interval is bounded on the right by $1 - \frac{1}{2} + \frac{1}{3}$, and on the left by $1 - \frac{1}{2} + \frac{1}{3} - \frac{1}{4}$. Each new interval is inside the one that it follows. Moreover, the width of the intervals is shrinking toward 0. The intervals form a nest, and, as we know, there is one and only one point inside the nest. The partial sums are crowding in toward this point as a limit,

111

so the series $1 - \frac{1}{2} + \frac{1}{3} - \frac{1}{4} + \ldots$ is a convergent series.

A similar argument applies to any series in which the terms decrease toward zero, and the signs are alternately $+$ and $-$. Every such series defines a nest of intervals, and converges to the single point that is inside the nest. This result, which we have established for the real number system, does not hold for the rational number system, because there it is not true that every nest of intervals has a point inside.

Another type of series that is easy to analyze is one in which all terms are positive, and the partial sums are bounded, that is, they are always less than some fixed number. The series $1 + \frac{1}{2} + \frac{1}{4} + \frac{1}{8} + \ldots$ is an example of this type, because all partial sums are less than 2. Let us represent the general series of this type by $a_1 + a_2 + a_3 + \ldots$ where the subscripts 1, 2, 3, etc. are labels to identify the position of each term in the series. The partial sums are $a_1, a_1 + a_2, a_1 + a_2 + a_3, \ldots$ Since we get each partial sum from the one that precedes it by adding a positive number, the partial sums form an increasing sequence. Let us represent the partial sums by the symbols $S_1, S_2, S_3, S_4, \ldots$. That is, $S_1 = a_1$, $S_2 = a_1 + a_2$, $S_3 = a_1 + a_2 + a_3$, and so on.

If we represent the partial sums as points on the line of real numbers, since the numbers are increasing we get a succession of points *moving gradually to the right*. S_2 is to the right of S_1, S_3 is to the right of S_2, and so on. However, since the sums are all less than some fixed number, they cannot move too far to the right. If the fixed number is represented by K on the number line, its position is an upper boundary beyond which the sequence of partial sums cannot go. Now we show how we can use K and the partial sums to define a nest of intervals. The points S_1 and K are the ends of an interval. This is the first interval of the nest. All the S points after S_1 lie to the right of S_1 and to the left of K, so they are inside this interval. Let us divide this interval in half. The points in the sequence of S's are moving to the right. Either they finally enter the second half of the interval, or they do not. If they do enter the second half, once they enter they stay there, because they keep moving to the right, and never

112

get past K. In that case we use this second half of the interval as the second interval of the nest. If the S points never enter the second half, that means they always remain in the first half. Then we use the first half as the second interval of the nest. Now we repeat the process. We divide the second interval of the nest in half, and pick one of the halves as the third interval of the nest. We choose the second half if the S's ultimately enter it. We choose the first half if they never enter the second half.

In this way we get a sequence of intervals with the characteristics of a nest: the intervals are one inside the other, and the width of the intervals is shrinking toward zero. Then there is a single real number that lies inside all the intervals of the nest. Since we know from the way in which we chose the intervals of this nest that the partial sums enter and remain in each of them, then the partial sums converge toward this single number as a limit. Therefore an infinite series of positive terms whose partial sums are bounded converges to a limit. This result can also be restated in terms of the sequence of partial sums alone, without reference to the series from which the sums were derived: Every increasing sequence of numbers that is bounded on the right converges to a limit.

The two types of convergent series just examined are only special cases. It is not difficult, however, to find a criterion by which all convergent series can be recognized. Suppose the series is represented by $a_1 + a_2 + a_3 \ldots$, where the terms may be either positive or negative. Whenever we form a partial sum, we are breaking the series up into two parts. The first part consists of a finite number of terms at the beginning of the series, taken in order, and added to get the partial sum. Let us call this part the head end of the series. The second part consists of all the remaining terms, that are not used to form this partial sum. Let us call this part the tail end of the series. We can designate the successive partial sums, formed from the head end as more and more terms are included in it, by S_1, S_2, S_3, etc. Let us call the corresponding tail ends T_1, T_2, T_3, etc. Then

$S_1 = a_1$, with tail end $T_1: a_2 + a_3 + a_4 \cdots$

$S_2 = a_1 + a_2$, with tail end $T_2: a_3 + a_4 + a_5 + \cdots$

$S_3 = a_1 + a_2 + a_3$, with tail end $T_3: a_4 + a_5 + a_6 + \cdots$

As we move along the sequence of partial sums, S_1, S_2, etc., we take one term at a time from the tail end and transfer it to the head end to be included in the partial sum. As a result, as n increases, the value of the partial sum, S_n, keeps changing. If the last term that is transferred is positive the change is an increase. If the term is negative, the change is a decrease. If we disregard the sign of the term we get a positive number that tells us the size of the change without regard to whether it is a decrease or increase. This positive number is called the absolute value of the change. Thus, an increase by $\frac{1}{2}$ or a decrease by $\frac{1}{2}$ both have an absolute value of $\frac{1}{2}$.

The series converges if the partial sums approach a limit. If the partial sums approach a limit, they become more and more nearly equal to that limit. This means that, as more and more terms are included in the partial sum, the sum changes less and less. And if n is taken large enough, the partial sum S_n is so close to the limit, that it changes very little no matter how many more terms are transferred from the tail end of the series to the head end. In fact, if n is large enough we can keep the absolute value of this change in the partial sum as small as we please. The partial sum S_n is equal to $a_1 + a_2 + \ldots + a_n$. The tail end T_n consists of the series $a_{n+1} + a_{n+2} + a_{n+3} + \ldots$. If we transfer the first p terms from the tail end to the head end, we add to S_n the sum $a_{n+1} + a_{n+2} + \ldots + a_{n+p}$. So, if the series converges, the absolute value of this sum must shrink toward zero as n increases, no matter how many terms from the tail end it includes. The converse is also true. If the absolute value of the sum of the first p terms of the tail end of the series shrinks to zero as n increases, no matter how large p is, then the series converges. This fact can be proved by showing that, under these conditions, there is a nest of intervals into which the partial sums crowd, so that they converge on the single point that is inside the nest. This criterion for a convergent series is known as the Cauchy criterion, and may be summed up somewhat carelessly in these words: in the real number system, an infinite series converges to a limit if and only if it has a shrinking tail end.

Limit Points and Neighborhoods

So far we have passed through four stages in the enlargement of our number system. We started with the system of natural numbers. Then by successive extensions, we obtained the integers, the rational numbers, and the real numbers. This sequence of extensions, besides showing us how our notion of number has been evolving, also served to introduce us to a variety of mathematical structures. In the natural number system, we first encountered the structure which we have labeled a *"number system"* and which is distinguished by its obedience to the five laws. In the system of integers we found an example of both a *group* and a *ring*. The system of rational numbers was our first example of a *field*. Now, in the system of real numbers, we shall get acquainted for the first time with another type of structure, a *topological space*. A real number is an infinite decimal, and an infinite decimal is an infinite sequence of finite decimals. This fact compelled us to look into the question of when an infinite sequence converges to a limit. Now, as we examine more closely the notion of a limit, it will lead us to the concept of a topological space.

Suppose we look at the sequence of numbers, $1, \frac{1}{2}, \frac{1}{3}, \frac{1}{4}, \ldots$, in which the nth number is $\frac{1}{n}$. As n increases, these numbers become smaller and smaller and approach 0 as a limit. If we represent the numbers in the sequence as points on a line, the fact that they approach 0 as a limit shows up in the fact that the points crowd in toward the zero point. This crowding can be described without any reference to the order in which the numbers are arranged in the sequence. In fact, let us discard the sequence and merely think of the numbers as the set of points on the line. Let us give this particular set the name A. To define in what sense the points in the set A crowd in toward the zero point, we first introduce the notion of a neighborhood of a point.

A neighborhood of a point consists of all the points that surround it and are close to it. To make this concept more precise, we have to indicate what we mean by *close*. So we specify degrees of closeness, and each such specification defines a particular neighborhood. For example, we define a neighborhood of zero when we say it consists of all the points whose distance from zero is less than 1. This neighborhood includes all points that are larger than (to the right of) -1 but less than (to the left of) $+1$. In the diagram, we see this neighborhood as the interval between -1 and $+1$, not including its endpoints. We represent this neighborhood

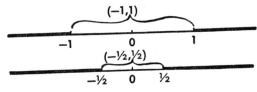

Neighborhoods of zero

by the symbol $(-1, 1)$, in which its boundary points are shown. We define another neighborhood of zero when we specify that it consists of all points whose distance from zero is less than $\frac{1}{2}$. This is a smaller neighborhood than the first one, and is included within it. All of its points lie between $-\frac{1}{2}$ and $+\frac{1}{2}$. We can represent it by the symbol $(-\frac{1}{2}, \frac{1}{2})$.

By picking any positive distance d, we can define a neighborhood of zero as the set of points lying between $-d$ and $+d$, and we represent it by the symbol $(-d, d)$. So we see that the zero point is surrounded by a multitude of neighborhoods of many sizes.

Now we can say exactly what is meant by the fact that the points in the set A $\left(A = \left\{ 1, \frac{1}{2}, \frac{1}{3}, \ldots \frac{1}{n}, \ldots \right\} \right)$ crowd in toward zero: If we pick any neighborhood of zero, no matter how small, all but a finite number of these points lie

116

within that neighborhood. If we choose smaller and smaller neighborhoods, we can exclude some of the points of the set A from the neighborhood. But, no matter how many we exclude, all but a finite number of the points are still inside. This is the meaning of the fact that 0 is the limit point of the set A.

Now let us examine a set in which we find crowding of a different kind. Let B stand for the set

$$\left\{1+\tfrac{1}{2}, 1+\tfrac{1}{3}, 2-\tfrac{1}{3}, 1+\tfrac{1}{4}, 2-\tfrac{1}{4}, \ldots, 1+\frac{1}{n}, 2-\frac{1}{n}, \ldots\right\}.$$

In this set, we find the points crowding around two points of the line, 1, and 2. Here we cannot say that every neighborhood of the point 1 includes all but a finite number of points in the set. In fact, while the neighborhood $(\tfrac{1}{2}, 1\tfrac{1}{2})$ includes an infinite number of points of the set B, it also excludes an infinite number, because there are multitudes of them clustering around the point 2. To distinguish this case from the preceding case, we call the points 1 and 2 *cluster points* of the set B. A point is a cluster point of a set of points if every neighborhood of the point includes an infinite number of points of the set. As we see, a set may have more than one cluster point. If a set is confined within a finite interval, and has only one cluster point, then that single cluster point is the limit point of the set.

As a contrast to the behavior of a limit point or a cluster point, let us examine the point -1 in relation to the set A. Surround the point -1 by the neighborhood that extends from $-1\tfrac{1}{2}$ to $-\tfrac{1}{2}$. Within this neighborhood, represented by the symbol $(-1\tfrac{1}{2}, -\tfrac{1}{2})$, there are no points of the set A. That is, the neighborhood $(-1\tfrac{1}{2}, -\tfrac{1}{2})$ excludes all points of the set A. On the other hand, there is no neighborhood of the point 0 that excludes all points of the set A. Similarly, there is no neighborhood of the point 1 that excludes all points of the set B, and there is no neighborhood of the point 2 that excludes all points of the set B. Because they have this property, a limit point and a cluster point are both examples of what we call a point of adherence of a set.

117

A point is called a *point of adherence* of a set of points if no neighborhood of the point excludes all points of the set. A point need not be a limit point or a cluster point of a set in order to be a point of adherence of the set. For example, the point $1\frac{1}{2}$ is not a cluster point of the set B, but it is a point of adherence. No neighborhood of $1\frac{1}{2}$ can exclude all points of the set B because the point $1\frac{1}{2}$ is itself a member of the set. The points of adherence of a set include all members of the set as well as cluster points that are not in the set. They are the points that cling to a set by either being in it or being crowded by it.

Closed Sets and Open Sets

With the help of the concept of point of adherence, we now define two special kinds of sets of points on the line. A set that contains all of its points of adherence is called a *closed set*. The set A, discussed in the paragraphs above, is not a closed set, because the point 0 is a point of adherence of the set but does not belong to it. However, if we enlarge the set by including 0 as a member, then the enlarged set is closed. Similarly, the set B is not closed. But the enlarged set formed by uniting B with the set $\{1, 2\}$ is closed. Another example of a closed set is the set of points between 0 and 1, *including the points 0 and 1*. Such a set is called a *closed interval*. The set which contains *all* the points on the line of real numbers is also a closed set. We can count the empty set as a closed set, too. It certainly includes all its points of adherence, because there aren't any.

If we delete from the real number line all the members of some closed set, what is left is called an *open set*. Using the terminology defined in Chapter II, we can say that an open set is the complement of a closed set. To see what an open set is like, we have to think of it in relation to the closed set which is its complement. Suppose S is an open set, and C is the closed set which is its complement. Any point of the open set S is not in the closed set C. Therefore any point in the open set S is not a point of adherence of C. (If it were, it would have to be in C, by the definition of a closed set.)

But if a point is not a point of adherence of C, then some neighborhood of the point contains no points of C. This neighborhood, which contains no points of C, must then be part of the open set S, which consists of all the points that are not in C. So we have discovered that every point of an open set is surrounded by an entire neighborhood that is also in the open set. This is a distinguishing feature of open sets on a line.

A neighborhood is itself an example of an open set. For example, the set of points between 0 and 1, *not including 0 and 1*, is an open set. It is called an *open interval* to distinguish it from the closed interval which does include both end points. Another example of an open set is the set formed by uniting into one set all points in any collection of open intervals. The whole line of real numbers is also an open set, because it is the complement of the empty set, which is a closed set. The empty set, too, is an open set, because it is the complement of the whole line, which is a closed set. We see then that the empty set and the whole line are both open and closed.

There are some sets that are neither open nor closed. For example, the set of points between 0 and 1, including the endpoint 0, but not including the endpoint 1, is neither open nor closed. It is not closed, because 1 is a point of adherence of the set, but doesn't belong to it. It is not open, because 0 is a point of adherence of the complement of the set, but does not belong to the complement, so the complement is not closed.

The collection of all open sets on the line has the following properties, some of which we have already noted:

1) The whole line, as well as the empty set, are open sets.
2) The union of any number of open sets is also an open set.
3) The set of points common to two open sets (the intersection of the two sets) is an open set.

Neighbors Make a Neighborhood

The significance of the concept of an open set is that it permits a generalization of the concept of neighborhood.

We have already seen that a neighborhood is an open set. Let us agree to extend the word neighborhood to include every open set. The effect of this generalization is to separate the notion of neighborhood from the idea of distance. Then a neighborhood becomes simply a collection of neighbors, with the characteristics of an open set. From this point of view, the whole line may be viewed as a system of interlocking neighborhoods or open sets. The interlocking neighborhoods on the line determine what is called its topological structure, and make it a topological space. They fix a pattern of relationships within the space just as the interlocking stitches in a sweater fix the pattern of the sweater.

In general, any set of objects is called a topological space if a collection of its subsets are singled out so that the collection has the three properties we found in the open sets on the line: 1) The whole space and the empty set belong to the collection; 2) The union of any number of sets in the collection is also in the collection; 3) The intersection of any two sets in the collection is also in the collection. When these three conditions are satisfied, the sets in the collection are called the "open sets" of the "space."

Under this definition, any collection of objects can be converted into a topological space, usually in more than one way. For example, let us consider the set $\{x, 2, \#, *\}$. Its elements were chosen arbitrarily, so they have no relationship to each other beyond the fact that they happen to have been thrown together in the same set. The set is a loose aggregation, and has no structure. However, the set acquires a structure, and the elements become related to each other as neighbors, as soon as we single out certain subsets that will be called neighborhoods or open sets.

For example, we might specify that these four sets should constitute the collection of open sets: $\{x, 2, \#, *\}$, $\{x, 2\}$, $\{\#, *\}$, and $\{\ \}$. This collection satisfies the three requirements listed above. 1) The whole space, $\{x, 2, \#, *\}$, and the empty set, $\{\ \}$, are members of the collection. 2) The union of any number of sets in the collection is also in the collection. For example, the union of $\{x, 2\}$ and $\{\#, *\}$ is $\{x, 2, \#, *\}$, which is in the collection. 3) The intersection of any two sets in the collection is also in the collection. For example, the intersection of $\{x, 2\}$ and $\{\#, *\}$ is the empty set $\{\ \}$, which is in the collection. Since the requirements are met, this collection of "open sets" defines a topological structure for the set $\{x, 2, \#, *\}$ and converts it into a topological space. The way the topological structure relates the elements of the space to each other as members of neighborhoods is indicated in the diagram below, where each open set is represented by a loop enclosing its members.

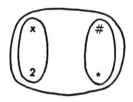

We can give the same set another, different topological structure by picking out other subsets to use as "open sets." We might, for example, decide that we want the collection of open sets to include all those listed above, and in addition the set $\{x, \#\}$. The inclusion of this one additional set among the open sets compels us to include more sets, in order to meet the three requirements. The union of $\{x, \#\}$ and $\{x, 2\}$ is $\{x, 2, \#\}$. To meet requirement 2), we must include it among the open sets. The intersection of $\{x, \#\}$ and $\{x, 2\}$ is the set $\{x\}$. To meet requirement 3), we must classify it as an open set. For similar reasons, we have to include $\{x, \#, *\}$ and $\{\#\}$ among the open sets. We find that all three requirements are met now by the enlarged collection consisting of these nine sets:

$$\{x, 2, \#, *\},\ \{x, 2\},\ \{\#, *\},\ \{\ \},$$
$$\{x, \#\},\ \{x, 2, \#\},\ \{x, \#, *\},\ \{x\},\ \{\#\}.$$

The enlarged collection of open sets gives the space a more complicated structure of interlocking neighborhoods, as shown in the diagram on page 122.

A third topological structure can be defined for the same

121

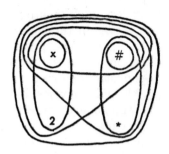

set by specifying that *every* subset shall belong to the collection of open sets. This definition meets the three requirements, because the whole set and the empty set are both subsets; the union of any number of subsets is a subset; and the intersection of any two subsets is a subset. Under this definition, the set of four elements becomes a topological space containing sixteen open sets, including the empty set. The three topological structures we have defined convert the same set of four elements into three different topological spaces. They are different as spaces because, in each of the topological structures, the elements hang together differently as members of interlocking neighborhoods.

Here is another example of a topological space. Consider all the straight lines that can be drawn in a plane parallel to some fixed direction. We can convert this set of lines into a topological space, in which each of the lines is a "point" of the space, by defining for the space a structure of interlocking open sets. Let an open set consist of a set of lines between any two lines, or a union of any number of such sets. In this space, a set of lines between any two lines is analogous to what we called an open interval in the real number system, namely, a set of points between any two points.

A more familiar looking example of a topological space is the circumference of a circle, in which arcs play the same role that intervals do on a straight line. On a circle, there are two arcs joining any two of its points. The interior (excluding the endpoints) of the arc may serve as an "open" arc just as the interior of a segment serves as an open interval on a straight line. An open set on the circle can then

122

be defined as the union of any number of such open arcs. With this definition, the circle is furnished with a topological structure that meets the three requirements listed on page 120. This topological structure on a circle can also be derived from the topological structure on a straight line in which each open set is a union of open intervals. Take a segment of a straight line, and loop it to make a circle by joining the two ends together. Then open intervals on the straight line become open arcs on the circle.

By isolating the topological structure of the real number system for separate study, mathematicians have obtained a deeper insight into the characteristics of that system. They could separate from each other those properties that the system has by virtue of the fact that it is a topological space, those that it has by virtue of the fact that it is a field, and those that it has because it happens to be both. The separate study of topological structures also develops a body of knowledge that is applicable to other topological spaces, no matter what the elements of these spaces may be.

Rubber-Sheet Geometry

Now that we have introduced the notion of a topological space, it is relevant to ask, "When are two topological spaces essentially the same?" The problem is analogous to the problem we encountered when we were talking about groups, rings, or fields, and has a similar answer. We said that two fields are essentially the same, or are isomorphic, if there is a one-to-one correspondence between them that preserves the field structure embodied in the operations of addition and multiplication. Similarly, we say that two topological spaces are essentially the same, or are *homeomorphic*, if there is a one-to-one correspondence between them that preserves the topological structure embodied in the system of interlocking open sets. That is, two topological spaces are homeomorphic if, under a reversible mapping which establishes a one-to-one correspondence between them, an open set in either space has as its image an open set in the other. For example, imagine the circumference of a circle being stretched like a rubber band, into a distorted shape. Each point of the circle may take up a new position. Distances between points change, but the interlocking system of open sets remains. As a result the distorted curve obtained is homeomorphic to the original circle. Because the topological structure of a space is not changed when it is stretched without tearing, the study of topological structure has sometimes been referred to as "rubber-sheet geometry."

DO IT YOURSELF

1. By an argument similar to the one used on page 94, prove that there is no rational number equal to the square root of 3.
2. Find the repeating decimal that represents the rational number $\frac{2}{13}$.
3. What rational number is represented by the repeating decimal .181818. . . . ?
4. Define a topological structure for the set of five elements $\{a, e, i, o, u\}$ by designating some but not all of the subsets as "open" sets. (See example on page 120.) Be sure your open sets meet the requirements for a topological structure listed on page 120. Which sets are closed sets (complements of open sets) in this structure?

CHAPTER VI

Spilling Into the Plane

IN THE system of rational numbers we were able to solve the equation $x^2 - 1 = 0$, but we were unable to solve the equation $x^2 - 2 = 0$. We remedied this defect by constructing a larger number system, the system of real numbers, in which the equation $x^2 - 2 = 0$ does have a solution. In fact, it has two solutions in the real number system, viz., $+\sqrt{2}$, and $-\sqrt{2}$. But the real number system has some defects of its own. For example, although the equation $x^2 + 1 = 0$ does not look any more complicated than the other two equations mentioned above, it has no solutions in the real number system. We can see why this is so, by restating the question that the equation asks us. First we add -1 to both sides of the equation, and we get the equivalent equation $x^2 = -1$. This equation says, "Find a number which, when multiplied by itself, gives -1 as the product." The real number 0 does not meet the requirement, because 0 multiplied by itself gives 0 as the product. A positive real number can not meet the requirement, because a positive number multiplied by itself gives a positive number as the product. A negative real number cannot answer the question either, because a negative number multiplied by itself also gives a positive product. For example $(-1) \cdot (-1) = +1$. So there is no real number that can satisfy the equation $x^2 + 1 = 0$, or $x^2 = -1$. Our next goal is to construct an expanded number system in which this equation does have a solution.

At each stage in the expansion of the number system so far we have represented numbers pictorially as points on a line. With the construction of the real number system, we finally achieved our purpose of having a number for every point on the line. Another possible goal for the next step in the expansion of the number system would be to spill over into the plane, by constructing a number system that gives us a number for every point in the plane. It turns out that these two goals coincide. We shall reach the goal of finding a solution to the equation $x^2 + 1 = 0$ by building a number system that supplies a number for every point in the plane.

Number Pairs and Arrows

The construction of a number system that has a number for every point in the plane will be carried out in two installments. We shall do only half of the job in this chapter, by creating an appropriate system of elements, and defining an addition operation on these elements. We shall finish the job in Chapter VIII when we define a multiplication operation for these elements. The elements we shall use are ordered pairs of real numbers, like $(0, 1)$, $(-2, 3\frac{1}{2})$, or $(1, \sqrt{2})$. We assign such a pair to each point in a plane by the familiar method used in elementary algebra to identify the co-ordinates of a point on a graph. First we draw in the plane a straight line called the x axis. We furnish it with a scale on which measurements can be made by assigning a real number to each point on the line, in the manner described in the preceding chapters. Then we draw another line passing through the 0 of the x axis, and crossing the axis at right angles. This new line is called the y axis. The point where the axes cross is called the *origin*. We put a scale on the y axis, too, using the origin as its zero point, and putting the positive numbers on the upper half of the axis.

Now we assign a pair of numbers to each point in the plane in the following way. Drop a perpendicular from a given point to the x axis. We can reach the given point from the origin by moving toward it in two steps. First move from the origin to the foot of the perpendicular. The distance moved supplies the first number of the ordered pair. It is a positive number if the motion is to the right of the origin. It is a negative number if the motion is to the left of the origin. Now, from the foot of the perpendicular, move along the perpendicular to the given point. The distance moved in this second step supplies the second number of the ordered pair. It is a positive number if the motion is up from the x axis. It is a negative number if

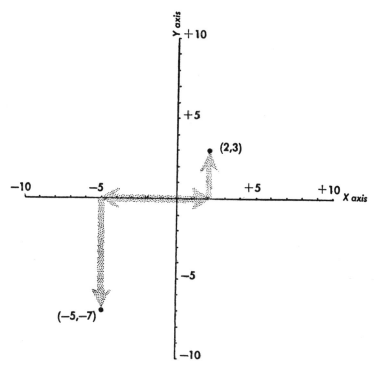

the motion is down from the x axis. The pair of numbers is written inside parentheses. The first number in the pair is called its x component. The second number is called its y component. The ordered pairs that belong to some points in the plane are shown in the diagram below. Notice that the ordered pair (0, 0) belongs to the origin. For all points on the x axis, the y component is zero. For all points on the y axis, the x component is zero. We are going to convert the system of ordered pairs of real numbers into a number system in its own right by giving it the necessary structure.

The point to which an ordered pair is assigned may be thought of as a picture of the pair. We can also associate another kind of picture with each pair in the following way. Draw an arrow from the origin to the point, with the arrowhead pointing away from the origin. We may think of the arrow as the second picture of the ordered pair. Each

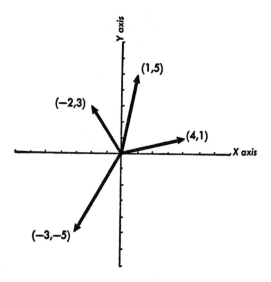

ordered pair, except (0, 0) has an arrow of its own. The arrow has a definite length, and a definite direction. We can even assign an arrow to the pair (0, 0) by giving it an arrow whose length is zero. However, we cannot assign any direction to this zero arrow.

Addition of Arrows

The representation of ordered pairs as arrows is very helpful, because it guides us to an appropriate definition of addition for our system of ordered pairs. There are many practical situations where we encounter just such arrows,

128

and where there is a natural kind of addition that takes place. For example, in physics, a force can be represented as an arrow. The length of the arrow indicates the strength of the force, and the direction of the arrow indicates the direction of the force. If two forces act on a body at the same point, the effect is the same as though the body were acted on by a single force called the *sum* or *resultant* of the two forces. One way to find this sum or resultant is to draw the two forces as arrows at the origin, and then complete the parallelogram that has the two arrows as sides. The diagonal of the parallelogram that can be drawn from the origin is the resultant of the two forces.

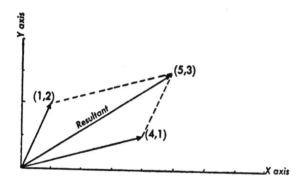

However, there is another, simpler way of getting the resultant, too. Each force, considered as an arrow, has an x component and a y component. To add the two forces, all we have to do is add their x components separately, and add their y components separately. For example, the forces being added in the diagram above can be represented as arrows, or as the ordered pairs, $(4, 1)$, and $(1, 2)$. The x components are 4 and 1, and the y components are 1 and 2. Adding them separately, we find that the resultant or sum of the forces belongs to the ordered pair $(5, 3)$. This example suggests how we should define addition of ordered pairs, if we want them to be useful for the solution of practical problems. We therefore give the following defini-

129

tion of addition in the new system: To add two ordered pairs, add their components separately. In symbols, this definition says, $(a, b) + (c, d) = (a + c, b + d)$. Because the sum of two ordered pairs is also an ordered pair, this addition is a binary operation.

There are several facts that we can observe about this binary operation immediately. First, it is associative. That is, $[(a, b) + (c, d)] + (e, f) = (a, b) + [(c, d) + (e, f)]$. This follows from the fact that we carry out the addition by adding the components, which are real numbers, and addition of real numbers is associative. For example,

$$[(2, 3) + (3, 1)] + (4, 8) = (5, 4) + (4, 8) = (9, 12).$$

But $(2, 3) + [(3, 1) + (4, 8)] = (2, 3) + (7, 9) = (9, 12)$, too. Secondly, the addition of ordered pairs is commutative. That is $(a, b) + (c, d) = (c, d) + (a, b)$. This follows from the fact that addition of real numbers is commutative. For example, $(2, 3) + (3, 1)$ and $(3, 1) + (2, 3)$ both yield the same sum, $(5, 4)$. Third, the system has a zero element, because $(0, 0) + (a, b) = (0 + a, 0 + b) = (a, b)$. Finally, for each element in the system, there is a negative in the system, too, with the usual property that a negative is supposed to have. That is, the sum of any ordered pair and its negative is equal to the zero element. The negative of any ordered pair (a, b) is the ordered pair $(-a, -b)$. For example, the negative of $(2, 3)$ is $(-2, -3)$ because $(2, 3) + (-2, -3) = (0, 0)$. With these four characteristics, the system of number pairs we have constructed meets all the requirements for being an abelian group, with the group operation denoted by the plus sign.

With this observation, we complete the first half of the job of converting these elements into a number system. We shall go on with the second half of the job in Chapter VIII. Meanwhile we take a detour along a road pointed out by our system of arrows. As we follow this road we shall encounter some more mathematical structures that play an important part in modern mathematics.

130

Stretching the Arrows

In the diagram below we see an arrow representing the ordered pair (2, 1). If the arrow is stretched so that its length is doubled while its direction remains unchanged, we get a new arrow (the shaded arrow in the diagram). If the arrow is contracted to half its original length we also get an arrow pointing in the same direction. In the first case, the length of the arrow was multiplied by a factor of 2. In the second case it was multiplied by a factor of $\frac{1}{2}$. Because of this fact, it is natural to think of the operation of stretching or shrinking an arrow as a kind of multiplication of the arrow by a real number. To see how we may

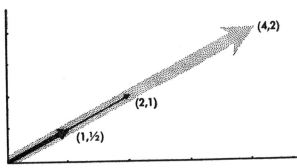

define the operation in terms of ordered pairs, notice that when the arrow (2, 1) was doubled, each of its components was doubled, giving the arrow (4, 2) as the result. So we define a special kind of multiplication for our system of ordered pairs as follows. To multiply an ordered pair of real numbers by a real number, multiply each of its components separately by that real number. In symbols, the definition says $a \cdot (b, c) = (a \cdot b, a \cdot c)$. It is important to notice that this kind of multiplication differs in one important respect from all the other multiplications defined so far in this book. In each of the earlier cases, the multiplication was an operation on two elements drawn from the same system. In this case, the two elements being multiplied are drawn from *two different systems*. One of the

131

multipliers is drawn from the field of real numbers. The other multiplier is drawn from the abelian group consisting of *ordered pairs* of real numbers. In order to sharpen the distinction between these two systems, we introduce some special names for them. We call the elements of the real number field *scalars*. The ordered pairs, or their pictorial representations as points in the plane or as arrows, will be called *vectors*. The kind of multiplication in which a vector is multiplied by a scalar to form a product which is also a vector is called *scalar multiplication*. We can verify from our definitions that scalar multiplication is *distributive with respect to vector addition*. That is, if s is a scalar, and (a, b) and (c, d) are vectors, then $s \cdot [(a, b) + (c, d)] = s \cdot (a, b) + s \cdot (c, d)$. To prove this rule, observe first that the expression on the left instructs us to do the vector addition first, and the scalar multiplication afterwards. So $s \cdot [(a, b) + (c, d)] = s \cdot (a + c, b + d) = (s \cdot [a + c], s \cdot [b + d]) = (s \cdot a + s \cdot c, s \cdot b + s \cdot d)$. The expression on the right instructs us to do two scalar multiplications first, and then add the results by vector addition. Following these instructions, we find that $s \cdot (a, b) + s \cdot (c, d) = (s \cdot a, s \cdot b) + (s \cdot c, s \cdot d) = (s \cdot a + s \cdot c, s \cdot b + s \cdot d)$. The proof is completed by observing that the two results are the same.

Scalar multiplication also satisfies another distributive law. It is distributive with respect to the addition of scalars. That is, if s and t are scalars, and (a, b) is a vector, then $(s + t) \cdot (a, b) = s \cdot (a, b) + t \cdot (a, b)$. To prove this rule, we observe that carrying out the indicated operations on both sides of the equals sign leads to the same result: $(s + t) \cdot (a, b) = ([s + t] \cdot a, [s + t] \cdot b) = (s \cdot a + t \cdot a, s \cdot b + t \cdot b)$. $s \cdot (a, b) + t \cdot (a, b) = (s \cdot a, s \cdot b) + (t \cdot a, t \cdot b) = (s \cdot a + t \cdot a, s \cdot b + t \cdot b)$.

Scalar multiplication also obeys a *mixed associative law*, in which two types of multiplication appear: 1) scalar multiplication, in which a scalar multiplies a vector, and 2) multiplication of scalars, in which a scalar multiplies a scalar. This law says that, if s and t are scalars, and (a, b)

132

is a vector, then $(s \cdot t) \cdot (a, b) = s \cdot [t \cdot (a, b)]$. To prove this law, observe that $(s \cdot t) \cdot (a, b) = ([s \cdot t] \cdot a, [s \cdot t] \cdot b) = (s \cdot t \cdot a, s \cdot t \cdot b)$. But $s \cdot [t \cdot (a, b)] = s \cdot (t \cdot a, t \cdot b) = (s \cdot [t \cdot a], s \cdot [t \cdot b]) = (s \cdot t \cdot a, s \cdot t \cdot b)$.

Scalar multiplication also has the property that the number 1, which is the unity element for multiplication of a scalar times a scalar, is also the unity element for multiplication of a scalar times a vector. This is seen from the fact that, if (a, b) is a vector, $1 \cdot (a, b) = (1 \cdot a, 1 \cdot b) = (a, b)$.

We shall now summarize these properties of scalar multiplication in a new abbreviated notation. So far we have always written a vector as an ordered pair, in which its two components are put on display. In the abbreviated notation, we represent a vector by a single symbol, with a little arrow over it to remind us that it stands for a vector. Thus, $\vec{x}$, $\vec{y}$, and $\vec{z}$ represent vectors. Symbols like r, s, and t, written without arrows, will represent scalars. In this notation, the properties of scalar multiplication are expressed in this form:

I. Distributive laws: $r \cdot (\vec{x} + \vec{y}) = r \cdot \vec{x} + r \cdot \vec{y}$

$$(r + s) \cdot \vec{x} = r \cdot \vec{x} + s \cdot \vec{x}$$

II. Mixed Associative law: $r \cdot (s \cdot \vec{x}) = (r \cdot s) \cdot \vec{x}$

III. Unity element: $1 \cdot \vec{x} = \vec{x}$

Because of the characteristics we have observed in the system of ordered pairs (pictured as arrows), this system serves as an example of the kind of mathematical structure that is called *a vector space*. The name vector space is used to describe any system of elements that has these properties: 1. It is an abelian group. 2. There is associated with this group another system of elements that is a field, and is called the scalar field. A scalar multiplication exists, in which a scalar from the field multiplies a vector from the

133

vector space, and the product is a vector in the vector space.
3. The scalar multiplication has properties I, II, and III
listed above.

Some Other Vector Spaces

Vector spaces won recognition as a special kind of structure worthy of separate study when mathematicians realized that there are many systems that have this kind of
structure. In the example that we have been observing,
each element in the vector space was an ordered pair of real
numbers. We can construct another vector space, by using
as elements ordered triples instead, like $(1, 3, -2)$. In
this system, each element has three components. We could
define vector addition and scalar multiplication for this
system in the same way that we did for the system of
ordered pairs: To add two vectors, add their separate components separately; to multiply by a scalar, multiply each
component separately by that scalar. For example, $(2, 3,
-5) + (1, 4, 2) = (3, 7, -3)$. And $2 \cdot (2, 3, -5) = (4, 6,
-10)$. With these definitions of vector addition and scalar
multiplication, the system of triples meets all the requirements for being a vector space. The system of ordered pairs
is an example of a vector space of two dimensions, and is
represented pictorially by points in a plane. The system of
ordered triples is an example of a vector space of three
dimensions, and can be represented pictorially by the points
in three dimensional space. By using ordered quadruples as
elements, we can construct a vector space of four dimensions. In general, we can construct a vector space of n
dimensions by using as elements ordered sets of real numbers with n numbers in each set. If we take $n = 1$, the
vectors are single real numbers, and the vector space is one
dimensional. In other words, the real number system may
be thought of as a vector space of one dimension whose
associated scalar field is also the real number system.

Another familiar system that has the structure of a
vector space is the system of all polynomials whose terms

134

are powers of x multiplied by some real number. Typical elements in this system look like this:

$$5x^4 + 3x^2 - 2x + 7$$

$$\sqrt{2}\, x^2 - 3x + 9$$

The two polynomials shown here are of the fourth and second degree respectively. There are also polynomials that do not contain x at all. They are just ordinary real numbers like 5, 7, -4, $\sqrt{3}$, and so on. We call them polynomials of zero degree. In this system, each polynomial is a vector. The real number system is the associated field of scalars. Vector addition is carried out by adding polynomials according to the rules taught in elementary algebra. The zero element for this addition is 0, a polynomial of no degree. Scalar multiplication is carried out by multiplying a polynomial by a real number according to the rules taught in elementary algebra. With these two operations, the system of polynomials meets all the requirements for being a vector space. In this vector space, each distinct power of x is a separate component. Any one polynomial contains only a finite number of components. But, since any positive power of x, like x^9, or x^{187}, may be used in a polynomial, there is an infinite number of components to choose from in constructing a polynomial. Therefore this system is an example of a vector space of *infinite dimension*.

The i, j, k Notation

In the study of physics it is found that such things as forces, velocities, and rotations can be represented as vectors in a three dimensional vector space. To carry out computations in this vector space the physicist uses a special notation in which all vectors are expressed in terms of three unit vectors called i, j, and k. They are defined as follows: $i = (1, 0, 0)$; $j = (0, 1, 0)$; $k = (0, 0, 1)$. The vector $(2, 3, 5)$ can be expressed in terms of these units in this way: $(2, 3, 5) = (2, 0, 0) + (0, 3, 0) + (0, 0, 5) = 2 \cdot (1, 0, 0) + 3 \cdot (0, 1, 0) + 5 \cdot (0, 0, 1) = 2i + 3j + 5k$.

135

In general, the vector $(a, b, c) = ai + bj + ck$. When this notation is used, all steps in vector addition and scalar multiplication become simple exercises in elementary high school algebra. For example:

Vector addition:

$$(2i + 3j + 5k) + (3i - 4j + 2k) = 5i - j + 7k$$

Scalar multiplication:

$$2(2i + 3j + 5k) = 4i + 6j + 10k$$

Mapping the Plane Into Itself

On page 131, we saw that multiplying the vector $(2, 1)$ by the scalar 2 has the effect of doubling the length of the associated arrow without changing its direction. If we multiply each of the vectors in the plane by 2, every one of the

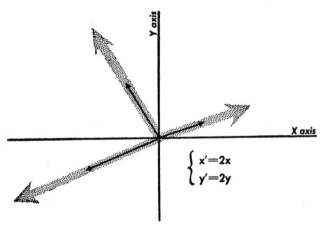

Solid arrow represents (x,y)

Shaded arrow represents (x′,y′)

associated arrows has its length doubled. The effect of the multiplication is to stretch the entire plane uniformly in all directions, so that each point of the plane is pulled to a new position, twice as far from the origin as it was before. We can represent a typical vector by the symbol (x, y), where x is its x component, and y is its y component. As a

136

result of the stretching, the vector (x, y) is changed into the vector $(2x, 2y)$. If we call the components of the new vector x' and y', the relationship between the old components and the new components is expressed in the equations: $x' = 2x$, and $y' = 2y$.

The stretching of the plane is an example of a mapping of the vector space into itself, whereby each element in the vector space is mapped into a particular image. Such a mapping is called a *transformation*. The equations above serve to define the transformation precisely, by giving directions for calculating, from the components of any vector, the components of the image into which it is mapped. If the stretching of the plane is one in which each arrow has its length tripled, the equations are $x' = 3x$ and $y' = 3y$. If we contract the plane, to shrink each arrow to half its size, the equations are $x' = \frac{1}{2}x$, and $y' = \frac{1}{2}y$. If we reverse the direction of each arrow in the vector space, the equations are $x' = -x$, and $y' = -y$. Such a reversal of direction is called a reflection. In general, equations of the form $x' = kx$ and $y' = ky$, where k is some fixed real number, define a stretching or contraction of all vectors, with or without a reversal of direction.

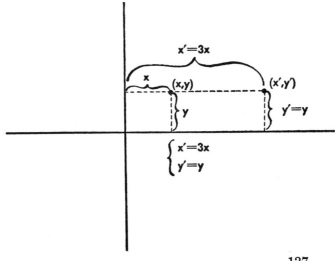

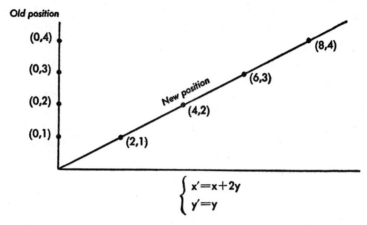

Old position

(0,4)
(0,3)
(0,2)
(0,1)

New position

(8,4)
(6,3)
(4,2)
(2,1)

$$\begin{cases} x' = x + 2y \\ y' = y \end{cases}$$

There are other transformations, too, that can be described pictorially in terms of motions or deformations of the plane. Each is defined precisely by an associated pair of equations that shows how the new components (of the image vectors under the mapping) are computed from the old components. The equations $x' = 3x$, $y' = y$ define a transformation which stretches the plane horizontally, while leaving each point as close to the x axis as it was before. The equations $x' = x + 2y$, $y' = y$ define a transformation which also leaves points at the same height above

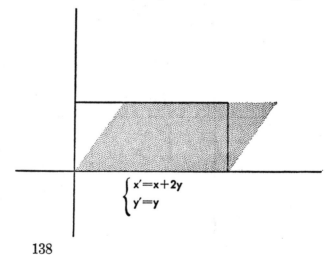

$$\begin{cases} x' = x + 2y \\ y' = y \end{cases}$$

138

or below the x axis, while moving them horizontally through varying distances that depend on their height. As a result this mapping moves the points of the y axis into new positions on a sloping line, as shown in the first diagram. The effect is a shearing of the plane, which deforms rectangles into parallelograms, as shown in the second diagram. The equations $x' = x \cos \theta - y \sin \theta$, $y' = x \sin \theta + y \cos \theta$ define a rotation of the plane around the origin as center. All these mappings are special examples of a particular family of transformations whose equations have this simple form:

$$x' = a_1x + a_2y$$
$$y' = b_1x + b_2y$$

Mappings that can be written in this form, where a_1, a_2, b_1, b_2 may be any fixed real numbers, are called *linear mappings*.

Another kind of mapping is obtained when the entire plane is moved in the direction of some particular vector through a distance equal to the length of that vector. Such a mapping is called a *translation*. For example, the equations $x' = x + 2$, $y' = y + 3$ define a translation that moves every point in the plane in the direction and through the distance specified by the vector $(2, 3)$. In general, equations of the form $x' = x + h$, $y' = y + k$, where h and k are fixed real numbers, represent translations of the plane. A more complicated type of transformation is obtained when a linear mapping is followed by a translation. Then the equations look like this:

$$x' = a_1x + a_2y + h$$
$$y' = b_1x + b_2y + k$$

Reversible Mappings

The mapping defined by the equations $x' = x + 2$, $y' = y + 3$ moves every point in the plane two units to the right and three units up. This mapping is easily reversed. If, after the mapping, each point is moved two units to the left and three units down, the points all return to their original

139

positions. The reversibility of the mapping can be expressed in terms of the equations, too. The equations show how to calculate the new components x' and y' from the old components x and y. If we solve the equations for x and y, we get equations in this form: $x = x' - 2$, $y = y' - 3$. These equations give directions for calculating the old components from the new, so they are the equations of the reverse mapping. In this reverse mapping, considered as a mapping in its own right, x' and y' are the components of a vector in its initial position, and x and y are the components in the final position. To conform to the original notation, in which the primed symbols are used to represent the new position, we represent the reverse mapping in this form: $x' = x - 2$, $y' = y - 3$. In general, for every translation, represented by the equations $x' = x + h$, $y' = y + k$ there is a reverse translation whose equations are $x' = x - h$, $y' = y - k$.

The Translations Form a Group

In the equations $x' = x + h$, $y' = y + k$, every time we pick definite values for h and k, we have equations representing some definite translation. For example, the pair of equations $x' = x + 2$, $y' = y + 3$ represents one translation. Let us call this translation P. The pair of equations $x' = x + 5$, $y' = y + 7$ represents another translation. Let us call it Q. If we take all possible values for the numbers h and k, we get all possible translations of the plane into itself. These translations form a system of elements in which an operation of multiplication can be defined.

Just as we did in the case of the symmetries of the triangle, back in Chapter III, we define the product of two translations as the result of performing one translation after another, with the second one taking over where the first one leaves off. The combined effect of the two translations is equivalent to a single transformation, which, in fact, is also a translation.

For example, suppose we designate by $Q * P$ the transformation we get when P is performed first, and Q is performed next on the results of P. P transforms components x and y by adding 2 and 3 to them respectively, so the new components are $x + 2$, and $y + 3$. Q transforms these components by adding 5 and 7 to them, respectively, so the final components are $x + 7$ and $y + 10$. So the equations for the product $Q * P$ are: $x' = x + 7$, $y' = y + 10$. These are of the form $x' = x + h$, $y' = y + k$, with the special values 7 and 10 for h and k. So $Q * P$ also belongs to the system of translations. Because the product of two translations is it-itself a translation, the operation $*$ is a binary operation in the system of translations. The operation is associative, because, if P, Q, and R are three translations, $(R * Q) * P$ and $R * (Q * P)$ both mean P followed by Q followed by R. The translation defined by the equations $x' = x + 0$, $y' = y + 0$ doesn't move the plane at all, and is the identity element for the operation $*$. If we designate it by I, then $P * I = I * P = P$. We have already observed that every translation is reversible. Let us designate by P^{-1} the translation that is the reverse of P. If it is applied after P, it brings every point in the plane back to its original position. So the product $P^{-1} * P$ is equal to the identity element I. Similarly, $P * P^{-1} = I$. So P^{-1} is the inverse of P with respect to the operation $*$. Because of these properties, the system of translations constitutes a group with respect to the operation $*$. In fact, it is an abelian group, because the operation turns out to be commutative.

The Linear Group

In the equations

$$x' = a_1 x + a_2 y$$
$$y' = b_1 x + b_2 y,$$

every time we pick definite values for a_1, a_2, b_1 and b_2, we get equations representing a particular linear mapping of the plane into itself. If we take all possible real values of a_1, a_2, b_1, and b_2, we get all possible linear mappings. They form a system of elements in which the operation $*$, defined in the same way as for translations, is a binary operation, because the product of two linear mappings is itself a linear mapping. For example, if P stands for the mapping

$$x' = 2x + 3y$$

$$y' = 5x - y$$

and Q stands for the mapping

$$x'' = 3x' + 4y',$$

$$y'' = 2x' + 7y'$$

we get the mapping $Q * P$ by applying the mapping Q to the results of P as follows:

$$x'' = 3(2x + 3y) + 4(5x - y) = 6x + 9y + 20x - 4y$$

$$y'' = 2(2x + 3y) + 7(5x - y) = 4x + 6y + 35x - 7y.$$

So the transformation $Q * P$ has the equations

$$x'' = 26x + 5y$$

$$y'' = 39x - y$$

These are the equations of a linear mapping in which a_1, a_2, b_1, and b_2 have the special values 26, 5, 39 and -1 respectively.

However, the system of all linear mappings does not form a group. It fails to qualify as a group because not all the linear mappings are reversible. The reason for this difficulty can be seen by comparing one of the troublesome linear mappings with a translation. A translation maps each point into an image in such a way that no two points have the same image. We can reverse the translation by carrying each point back to the single point of which it is the image. However, the linear mapping defined by the equations

$$x' = 0x + 0y = 0$$

$$y' = 0x + 0y = 0,$$

behaves differently. It carries all points into the origin. As a result, the origin is the image of not one point, but

142

many points. A many-to-one mapping, as we saw on page 15, is not reversible.

However, there are some linear mappings that are reversible. If we put aside those linear mappings that are not reversible, and keep only those that are reversible, then we get a subset of the system of linear mappings that does constitute a group. In this subset, every linear mapping has an inverse, and all the other requirements for qualifying as a group are satisfied. We can find out which linear mappings are reversible by actually trying to reverse one, and seeing what conditions must be fulfilled to attain success. Suppose we take the equations of a linear mapping in general form:

$$x' = a_1x + a_2y$$
$$y' = b_1x + b_2y.$$

To reverse the mapping means to solve for x and y in terms of x' and y'. Let us first write the equations with the x' and y' on the right hand side, and then solve for x and y by the usual method for solving simultaneous equations by eliminating one of the unknowns. To eliminate y, we multiply the first equation by b_2, multiply the second equation by $-a_2$, and then add the resulting equations:

$$\begin{array}{rcl} a_1b_2x + a_2b_2y &=& b_2x' \\ -a_2b_1x - a_2b_2y &=& -a_2y' \\ \hline a_1b_2x - a_2b_1x &=& b_2x' - a_2y' \end{array}$$

The distributive law permits us to rewrite the left hand side of the equation in factored form: $(a_1b_2 - a_2b_1)x = b_2x' - a_2y'$. The next step in solving for x would be to divide both sides of the equation by $(a_1b_2 - a_2b_1)$ to get as a result

$$x = \frac{b_2x' - a_2y'}{a_1b_2 - a_2b_1}$$

However, this step is not always possible. We know from our discussion on page 74 that division makes sense only when the divisor is not zero. So we can succeed in reversing the linear mapping if and only if $a_1b_2 - a_2b_1$ is not equal to zero. The number $a_1 b_2 - a_2 b_1$ is called the determinant of the linear mapping. So we can say that a linear mapping is reversible if and only if its determinant is different from zero. For example, suppose linear mappings A and B are defined as follows:

$$A: \begin{cases} x' = 2x + 3y \\ y' = 4x + 6y \end{cases} \qquad B: \begin{cases} x' = 2x - 3y \\ y' = 3x + y \end{cases}$$

The determinant of mapping A is $2 \cdot 6 - 3 \cdot 4 = 0$, so A is not a reversible mapping. The determinant of mapping B is $2 \cdot 1 - (-3) \cdot 3 = 11$, which is different from zero, so B is a reversible mapping. In fact, if we solve for x and y in terms of x' and y', we get

$$x = \frac{1}{11} x' + \frac{3}{11} y'$$

$$y = \frac{-3}{11} x' + \frac{2}{11} y'.$$

These equations have the right form to qualify as a linear mapping, which we may designate as B^{-1}, or the inverse of B. Moreover, B^{-1} is reversible, because solving for x' and y' leads back again to the original equations of B.

The system of reversible linear mappings is known as the *linear group*. It includes all rotations, stretches, and shears of the plane.

If a reversible linear mapping is followed by a translation, the product is called an *affine* transformation. The system of all such products also turns out to be a group, and is known as the affine group. If a uniform stretching of the plane is followed by a translation, the product is called a *similitude*. The system of all such products constitutes another group, known as the group of similitudes. If we put together in one set of transformations all rotations, translations, and reflections, this set, too, is a group, and is known as the *Euclidean* group.

What Is Geometry?

The fact that transformations of a plane into itself can be associated with each other in families of transformations, some of which have a group structure, has led to a new insight into the meaning of geometry. In the geometry we study in high school, considerable time is devoted to the study of congruent figures. We try to find out what figures are congruent to each other. We also investigate properties of a figure that it has in common with any other figure to which it is congruent. Such properties include lengths of corresponding lines, sizes of corresponding angles, area, etc. Two figures were defined as being congruent if they could be made to coincide. This definition implied the use of a motion to carry one figure onto the other. To assure ourselves that the figure would not be deformed while it was being moved, we calmed our fears with the "axiom" that a geometric figure can be moved from place to place without changing its form or size. The effect of this axiom was to banish from the realm of legitimate motions all stretches and shears. At the same time, it singled out as the only legitimate motions those that we have called rotations, translations and reflections. But these are the motions that make up the Euclidean group of transformations. This fact makes it possible to define more precisely what is meant by congruence. Two figures are congruent if one can be mapped onto the other by a transformation that belongs to the Euclidean group. This definition also gives a new meaning to such concepts as length, area, and so on. They turn out to be among the characteristics of a figure that remain unchanged when it is transformed by a mapping that belongs to the Euclidean group.

Another subject treated in high school geometry is that of similar figures. The concept of similarity can also be defined in terms of a group of transformations. Two figures are similar if one can be mapped onto the other by means of a transformation that belongs to the group of similitudes. A similitude does not leave the length of a line unchanged, but it does leave unchanged such things as angles, and ratios of lengths. The fact that the two traditional concerns of plane geometry can be described best in terms of groups of transformations has led to the modern notion of what a geometry is. A geometry is now defined as the study of figures which can be mapped into each other by a group of transformations, and of the properties of figures that remain unchanged when the transformations in the group are applied. In the sense of this definition, what we studied in high school was not geometry, but *some geometries*. When we studied congruence, we were studying Euclidean geometry, associated with the Euclidean group. When we studied similarity, we were studying a different geometry, associated with the group of similitudes. Moreover, there are other geometries which we did not study in high school at all. For example, there is an *affine geometry* associated with the affine group. Because there are many groups that may operate on the same vector space, there is a multiplicity of geometries belonging to one and the same space.

DO IT YOURSELF

1. Use the definition of vector addition given on page 130 to find the following vector sums:

    $(3, 2) + (-1, 2)$ $(8, -5) + (-5, 8)$

    $(4, 7) + (-4, -7)$ $(2, 0) + (0, 3)$

2. Use the definition of vector addition to prove that $(a, b) + (c, d) = (c, d) + (a, b)$. (Commutative Law of Addition)

3. Locate the points $(2, 3)$, $(-5, 4)$, and $(-6, -2)$ on a graph with coordinates measured from an x axis and a y axis that are perpendicular to each other. Carry out the following scalar multiplications, and locate the products on the graph: $3 \cdot (2, 3)$; $2 \cdot (-5, 4)$; $-\frac{1}{2} \cdot (-6, -2)$. Verify from the graph that the first two scalar multiplications change the length of the arrow belonging to the vector, without changing its direction. Verify that the

146

third one changes the length and reverses the direction.

4. Represent these three-dimensional vectors in the i, j, k notation:

$$(4, 6, 1) \qquad (-2, 1, 0) \qquad (0, 5, 7)$$

5. Two linear mappings P and Q (mapping a plane into itself) are defined as follows. Find the equations that define the product $Q * P$.

$$P: \begin{cases} x' = x + y \\ y' = x - y \end{cases} \qquad Q: \begin{cases} x' = 2x + y \\ y' = x - 3y \end{cases}$$

Find the equations that define the product $P * Q$. Is $Q * P = P * Q$? Is the operation $*$ for such linear mappings commutative?

6. Find the inverse of the mapping P defined in question 5.

CHAPTER VII

The Rank and File: Matrices

IN THIS chapter we re-examine from another point of view the linear mappings of a plane into itself. In the course of this re-examination we shall get acquainted with another type of mathematical structure that is important. At the same time we shall acquire some equipment that will be useful to us in the next chapter where we finish the job of constructing a number system that supplies a number for every point in the plane.

Some typical linear mappings of the plane are listed below, with a capital letter assigned to each one as its name:

$$P: \begin{cases} x' = 1x + 1y \\ y' = 1x - 1y \end{cases} \quad Q: \begin{cases} x' = 2x + 1y \\ y' = 1x - 3y \end{cases}$$

$$O: \begin{cases} x' = 0x + 0y \\ y' = 0x + 0y \end{cases} \quad I: \begin{cases} x' = 1x + 0y \\ y' = 0x + 1y \end{cases}$$

The mapping called O could have been written more briefly in the form $x' = 0$, $y' = 0$. Similarly, the mapping called I could have been written as $x' = x$, $y' = y$. However, showing the zero coefficients explicitly, as we have in the longer way of writing them, has the advantage of stressing the fact that all linear mappings have the same form. In each mapping, the new x and the new y are obtained by adding some multiple of the old x to some multiple of the old y. Two different linear mappings differ from each other only by

148

virtue of the fact that they use different multiples. What distinguishes one linear mapping from another, then, is the set of four coefficients that appear in the equations of the mapping. This fact suggests that we can represent a mapping in an abbreviated notation in which we delete the letters x, y, x' and y', and merely list these four coefficients, arranging them in a square array, just as they are arranged in the equations written above. Such a square array of numbers is called a *matrix*. In this case, because the matrix has two rows and two columns, we call it a 2 by 2 matrix. Every linear mapping of the plane is associated with such a 2 by 2 matrix, and, vice versa, every 2 by 2 matrix of real numbers belongs to some linear mapping of the plane. To show this correspondence, we shall use as the name of a matrix the name of the mapping that it belongs to. Here are the matrices of the mappings P, Q, O, and I:

$$P = \begin{vmatrix} 1 & 1 \\ 1 & -1 \end{vmatrix} \quad Q = \begin{vmatrix} 2 & 1 \\ 1 & -3 \end{vmatrix} \quad O = \begin{vmatrix} 0 & 0 \\ 0 & 0 \end{vmatrix} \quad I = \begin{vmatrix} 1 & 0 \\ 0 & 1 \end{vmatrix}$$

Matrices Form a Vector Space

Now that we have a collection of matrices, we can disregard their origin as sets of coefficients belonging to linear mappings, and may think of them as constituting an independent system of elements. We proceed to give this system a structure in a simple and natural way. We convert it into a vector space by methods like those we used in the last chapter. Just as the vector $(2, 3)$ is made up of two components, each distinguished by the place it occupies in the ordered pair, each matrix is made up of four components, each distinguished by the place it occupies in the square array. So we can define addition of matrices the way we defined addition of ordered pairs. *To add two matrices, add the corresponding components separately.* We can also define a scalar multiplication for matrices, using the field of real numbers as the field of scalars, in the same way that we defined scalar multiplication for ordered pairs. *To multiply a matrix by a scalar, multiply each of its components by that scalar.* Examples of addition and scalar multiplication for matrices are shown below:

$$P + Q = \begin{vmatrix} 1 & 1 \\ 1 & -1 \end{vmatrix} + \begin{vmatrix} 2 & 1 \\ 1 & -3 \end{vmatrix} = \begin{vmatrix} 1+2 & 1+1 \\ 1+1 & (-1)+(-3) \end{vmatrix} = \begin{vmatrix} 3 & 2 \\ 2 & -4 \end{vmatrix}$$

$$2 \cdot Q = 2 \cdot \begin{vmatrix} 2 & 1 \\ 1 & -3 \end{vmatrix} = \begin{vmatrix} 2(2) & 2(1) \\ 2(1) & 2(-3) \end{vmatrix} = \begin{vmatrix} 4 & 2 \\ 2 & -6 \end{vmatrix}$$

With addition and scalar multiplication defined in this way, the system of 2 by 2 matrices becomes a vector space. To verify this fact, we have to show that it has all the characteristics of a vector space, listed on page 133. First, we observe that it is an abelian group with respect to addition. This is proved below by showing that addition is associative and commutative, that it has a zero element, and that every matrix has a negative:

Addition is associative:

$$\text{Let } P = \begin{vmatrix} a_1 & a_2 \\ b_1 & b_2 \end{vmatrix} \qquad Q = \begin{vmatrix} c_1 & c_2 \\ d_1 & d_2 \end{vmatrix} \qquad R = \begin{vmatrix} e_1 & e_2 \\ f_1 & f_2 \end{vmatrix}$$

$$(P + Q) + R = \begin{vmatrix} a_1 + c_1 & a_2 + c_2 \\ b_1 + d_1 & b_2 + d_2 \end{vmatrix} + \begin{vmatrix} e_1 & e_2 \\ f_1 & f_2 \end{vmatrix}$$

$$\begin{vmatrix} (a_1 + c_1) + e_1 & (a_2 + c_2) + e_2 \\ (b_1 + d_1) + f_1 & (b_2 + d_2) + f_2 \end{vmatrix}$$

$$P + (Q + R) = \begin{vmatrix} a_1 & a_2 \\ b_1 & b_2 \end{vmatrix} + \begin{vmatrix} c_1 + e_1 & c_2 + e_2 \\ d_1 + f_1 & d_2 + f_2 \end{vmatrix}$$

$$\begin{vmatrix} a_1 + (c_1 + e_1) & a_2 + (c_2 + e_2) \\ b_1 + (d_1 + f_1) & b_2 + (d_2 + f_2) \end{vmatrix}$$

But $(a_1 + c_1) + e_1 = a_1 + (c_1 + e_1)$, etc., because addition of real numbers is associative. Therefore $(P + Q) + R = P + (Q + R)$.

Addition is commutative:

150

$$P + Q = \begin{vmatrix} a_1 & a_2 \\ b_1 & b_2 \end{vmatrix} + \begin{vmatrix} c_1 & c_2 \\ d_1 & d_2 \end{vmatrix} = \begin{vmatrix} a_1 + c_1 & a_2 + c_2 \\ b_1 + d_1 & b_2 + d_2 \end{vmatrix}$$

$$Q + P = \begin{vmatrix} c_1 & c_2 \\ d_1 & d_2 \end{vmatrix} + \begin{vmatrix} a_1 & a_2 \\ b_1 & b_2 \end{vmatrix} = \begin{vmatrix} c_1 + a_1 & c_2 + a_2 \\ d_1 + b_1 & d_2 + b_2 \end{vmatrix}$$

But $a_1 + c_1 = c_1 + a_1$, etc., because addition of real numbers is commutative. Therefore $P + Q = Q + P$.

There is a zero element:

$$0 + P = \begin{vmatrix} 0 & 0 \\ 0 & 0 \end{vmatrix} + \begin{vmatrix} a_1 & a_2 \\ b_1 & b_2 \end{vmatrix} = \begin{vmatrix} 0 + a_1 & 0 + a_2 \\ 0 + b_1 & 0 + b_2 \end{vmatrix}$$

$$= \begin{vmatrix} a_1 & a_2 \\ b_1 & b_2 \end{vmatrix} = P$$

Therefore the matrix $0 = \begin{vmatrix} 0 & 0 \\ 0 & 0 \end{vmatrix}$ is the zero element for matrix addition, and is called the zero matrix.

Every matrix has a negative:

In fact, the negative of $\begin{vmatrix} a_1 & a_2 \\ b_1 & b_2 \end{vmatrix}$ is $\begin{vmatrix} -a_1 & -a_2 \\ -b_1 & -b_2 \end{vmatrix}$

because $\begin{vmatrix} a_1 & a_2 \\ b_1 & b_2 \end{vmatrix} + \begin{vmatrix} -a_1 & -a_2 \\ -b_1 & -b_2 \end{vmatrix} = \begin{vmatrix} a_1 + (-a_1) & a_2 + (-a_2) \\ b_1 + (-b_1) & b_2 + (-b_2) \end{vmatrix}$

$$= \begin{vmatrix} 0 & 0 \\ 0 & 0 \end{vmatrix} = \text{the zero matrix}$$

We observe next that scalar multiplication for matrices obeys the two distributive laws, the mixed associative law, and the law that the number 1 serves as a unity element for scalar multiplication:

Distributive laws:

$$r(P + Q) = r \left(\begin{vmatrix} a_1 & a_2 \\ b_1 & b_2 \end{vmatrix} + \begin{vmatrix} c_1 & c_2 \\ d_1 & d_2 \end{vmatrix} \right) = r \begin{vmatrix} a_1 + c_1 & a_2 + c_2 \\ b_1 + d_1 & b_2 + d_2 \end{vmatrix}$$

$$= \begin{vmatrix} r(a_1 + c_1) & r(a_2 + c_2) \\ r(b_1 + d_1) & r(b_2 + d_2) \end{vmatrix} = \begin{vmatrix} ra_1 + rc_1 & ra_2 + rc_2 \\ rb_1 + rd_1 & rb_2 + rd_2 \end{vmatrix}$$

$$rP + rQ = r\begin{vmatrix} a_1 & a_2 \\ b_1 & b_2 \end{vmatrix} + r\begin{vmatrix} c_1 & c_2 \\ d_1 & d_2 \end{vmatrix}$$

$$= \begin{vmatrix} ra_1 & ra_2 \\ rb_1 & rb_2 \end{vmatrix} + \begin{vmatrix} rc_1 & rc_2 \\ rd_1 & rd_2 \end{vmatrix} = \begin{vmatrix} ra_1 + rc_1 & ra_2 + rc_2 \\ rb_1 + rd_1 & rb_2 + rd_2 \end{vmatrix}$$

Therefore $r(P + Q) = rP + rQ$.

$$(r + s)P = (r + s)\begin{vmatrix} a_1 & a_2 \\ b_1 & b_2 \end{vmatrix} = \begin{vmatrix} (r + s)a_1 & (r + s)a_2 \\ (r + s)b_1 & (r + s)b_2 \end{vmatrix}$$

$$= \begin{vmatrix} ra_1 + sa_1 & ra_2 + sa_2 \\ rb_1 + sb_1 & rb_2 + sb_2 \end{vmatrix}.$$

$$rP + sP = r\begin{vmatrix} a_1 & a_2 \\ b_1 & b_2 \end{vmatrix} + s\begin{vmatrix} a_1 & a_2 \\ b_1 & b_2 \end{vmatrix}$$

$$= \begin{vmatrix} ra_1 & ra_2 \\ rb_1 & rb_2 \end{vmatrix} + \begin{vmatrix} sa_1 & sa_2 \\ sb_1 & sb_2 \end{vmatrix}$$

$$= \begin{vmatrix} ra_1 + sa_1 & ra_2 + sa_2 \\ rb_1 + sb_1 & rb_2 + sb_2 \end{vmatrix}$$

Therefore $(r + s)P = rP + sP$.

Mixed associative law:

$$r(sP) = r\left(s\begin{vmatrix} a_1 & a_2 \\ b_1 & b_2 \end{vmatrix}\right) = r\begin{vmatrix} sa_1 & sa_2 \\ sb_1 & sb_2 \end{vmatrix}$$

$$= \begin{vmatrix} r(sa_1) & r(sa_2) \\ r(sb_1) & r(sb_2) \end{vmatrix} = \begin{vmatrix} rsa_1 & rsa_2 \\ rsb_1 & rsb_2 \end{vmatrix}$$

$$(rs)P = (rs)\begin{vmatrix} a_1 & a_2 \\ b_1 & b_2 \end{vmatrix} = \begin{vmatrix} (rs)a_1 & (rs)a_2 \\ (rs)b_1 & (rs)b_2 \end{vmatrix}$$

$$= \begin{vmatrix} rsa_1 & rsa_2 \\ rsb_1 & rsb_2 \end{vmatrix}$$

Therefore $r(sP) = (rs)P$.

Unity element for scalar multiplication:

$$1 \cdot P = 1 \cdot \begin{vmatrix} a_1 & a_2 \\ b_1 & b_2 \end{vmatrix} = \begin{vmatrix} 1a_1 & 1a_2 \\ 1b_1 & 1b_2 \end{vmatrix} = \begin{vmatrix} a_1 & a_2 \\ b_1 & b_2 \end{vmatrix} = P$$

Multiplication of Matrices

In the last chapter we defined an operation of multiplication for linear mappings. Since each mapping has an associated matrix, we can transfer this operation to the matrices, and in this way define a multiplication operation for matrices. First, let us write down two matrices P and Q, and the mappings that are associated with them:

$$P = \begin{vmatrix} a_1 & a_2 \\ b_1 & b_2 \end{vmatrix} \qquad \text{associated} \atop \text{mapping} \qquad \begin{cases} x'' = a_1 x' + a_2 y' \\ y'' = b_1 x' + b_2 y' \end{cases}$$

$$Q = \begin{vmatrix} c_1 & c_2 \\ d_1 & d_2 \end{vmatrix} \qquad\qquad\qquad \begin{cases} x' = c_1 x + c_2 y \\ y' = d_1 x + d_2 y \end{cases}$$

To get the product mapping $P * Q$, we first perform the mapping Q, and then perform the mapping P on the new components we get as a result of having used Q.

$$x'' = a_1(c_1x + c_2y) + a_2(d_1x + d_2y) = a_1c_1x + a_1c_2y + a_2d_1x + a_2d_2y$$

$$y'' = b_1(c_1x + c_2y) + b_2(d_1x + d_2y) = b_1c_1x + b_1c_2y + b_2d_1x + b_2d_2y$$

By rearranging the terms to bring the x terms together, and the y terms together, and then factoring out the x and y, we find that the product mapping $P * Q$ takes this form:

$$x'' = (a_1c_1 + a_2d_1)x + (a_1c_2 + a_2d_2)y$$

$$y'' = (b_1c_1 + b_2d_1)x + (b_1c_2 + b_2d_2)y$$

The matrix that belongs to this mapping is

153

$$\begin{vmatrix} a_1c_1 + a_2d_1 & a_1c_2 + a_2d_2 \\ b_1c_1 + b_2d_1 & b_1c_2 + b_2d_2 \end{vmatrix}.$$

We call it the product matrix, and designate it by PQ. (We omit the $*$ just as in elementary algebra it is customary to omit the multiplication sign.)

Now, by comparing the matrix PQ with the matrices P and Q, we can observe a simple rule by which the multiplication can be carried out without reference to the equations of the mappings. Notice that in the product matrix PQ, the component in the *first row* and *first* column is $a_1c_1 + a_2d_1$. This expression can be obtained from the pairs (a_1, a_2) and (c_1, d_1) by first multiplying corresponding terms in the pairs, and then adding the products. The pair (a_1, a_2) is the *first row* of matrix P. The pair (c_1, d_1) is the *first column* of the matrix Q. So we get the component in the first row and first column of the product PQ by multiplying corresponding components of the first row of P and the first column of Q, and adding the results. In order to be able to refer to it in fewer words, let us designate this kind of operation as multiplication of the first row of P by the first column of Q. We can now use this language to describe the procedure for getting all the components of the product matrix. To get the component in the first row and second column, multiply the first row of P by the second column of Q. To get the component in the second row and first column, multiply the second row of P by the first column of Q. To get the component in the second row and second column, multiply the second row of P by the second column of Q. In general, to get the component of the product matrix PQ that is in any particular row and column, multiply the corresponding row of P by the corresponding column of Q.

If we apply this rule for multiplying matrices to get the product QP, we find that

$$QP = \begin{vmatrix} c_1 & c_2 \\ d_1 & d_2 \end{vmatrix} \cdot \begin{vmatrix} a_1 & a_2 \\ b_1 & b_2 \end{vmatrix} = \begin{vmatrix} c_1a_1 + c_2b_1 & c_1a_2 + c_2b_2 \\ d_1a_1 + d_2b_1 & d_1a_2 + d_2b_2 \end{vmatrix}.$$

Notice that this product is not the same as PQ, so matrix multiplication is *not commutative*.

The Matrices Form a Ring

Although matrix multiplication is not commutative, it is associative. We do not have to give a special proof of this fact, because we have already observed that the operation $*$, performed on linear mappings, is associative, and matrix multiplication is merely another way of expressing the same operation. It is also possible to show that matrix multiplication is distributive with respect to matrix addition. Consequently, the system of 2 by 2 matrices meets all the requirements for being a ring, just as the natural numbers, the integers, the rational numbers, and the real numbers did. However, unlike these other systems, it is not a commutative ring, since matrix multiplication is not commutative.

There is a unity element for matrix multiplication. In fact, the unity element is the matrix which we have called I. Since multiplication is not, in general, commutative, we have to verify separately that I behaves as a unity element when it is used as a multiplier either from the left or from the right.

$$IP = \begin{vmatrix} 1 & 0 \\ 0 & 1 \end{vmatrix} \cdot \begin{vmatrix} a_1 & a_2 \\ b_1 & b_2 \end{vmatrix} = \begin{vmatrix} 1a_1 + 0b_1 & 1a_2 + 0b_2 \\ 0a_1 + 1b_1 & 0a_2 + 1b_2 \end{vmatrix}$$

$$= \begin{vmatrix} a_1 & a_2 \\ b_1 & b_2 \end{vmatrix} = P$$

$$PI = \begin{vmatrix} a_1 & a_2 \\ b_1 & b_2 \end{vmatrix} \cdot \begin{vmatrix} 1 & 0 \\ 0 & 1 \end{vmatrix} = \begin{vmatrix} a_1 \cdot 1 + a_2 \cdot 0 & a_1 \cdot 0 + a_2 \cdot 1 \\ b_1 \cdot 1 + b_2 \cdot 0 & b_1 \cdot 0 + b_2 \cdot 1 \end{vmatrix}$$

$$= \begin{vmatrix} a_1 & a_2 \\ b_1 & b_2 \end{vmatrix} = P$$

Therefore $IP = PI = P$.

It is natural to ask whether the ring of 2 by 2 matrices is

also a field. We find that it is not a field, because it contains zero divisors, and a field may not have zero divisors, as we saw on page 87. Recall that zero divisors are non-zero elements that have a zero product. The matrices $\begin{vmatrix} 0 & 2 \\ 0 & 0 \end{vmatrix}$ and $\begin{vmatrix} 0 & 3 \\ 0 & 0 \end{vmatrix}$ are different from the zero matrix, but their product is equal to the zero matrix:

$$\begin{vmatrix} 0 & 2 \\ 0 & 0 \end{vmatrix} \cdot \begin{vmatrix} 0 & 3 \\ 0 & 0 \end{vmatrix} = \begin{vmatrix} 0 \cdot 0 + 2 \cdot 0 & 0 \cdot 3 + 2 \cdot 0 \\ 0 \cdot 0 + 0 \cdot 0 & 0 \cdot 3 + 0 \cdot 0 \end{vmatrix} = \begin{vmatrix} 0 & 0 \\ 0 & 0 \end{vmatrix} = 0$$

In fact, each of these matrices has the peculiar property that when it is multiplied by itself, the product is zero. If we use the letter T to represent the matrix $\begin{vmatrix} 0 & 2 \\ 0 & 0 \end{vmatrix}$, then

$$T^2 = T \cdot T = \begin{vmatrix} 0 & 2 \\ 0 & 0 \end{vmatrix} \cdot \begin{vmatrix} 0 & 2 \\ 0 & 0 \end{vmatrix} = \begin{vmatrix} 0 \cdot 0 + 2 \cdot 0 & 0 \cdot 2 + 2 \cdot 0 \\ 0 \cdot 0 + 0 \cdot 0 & 0 \cdot 2 + 0 \cdot 0 \end{vmatrix}$$

$$= \begin{vmatrix} 0 & 0 \\ 0 & 0 \end{vmatrix} = 0$$

An element like T that has the property that there is a power of it that is equal to zero is called a *nilpotent* element. In the rings we met before, the zero element itself was the only nilpotent element. However, there are many rings which, like the ring of 2 by 2 matrices, have nilpotent elements that are different from zero.

The Matrices Form an Algebra

The ring of 2 by 2 matrices has a double structure. With matrix addition and scalar multiplication, it has the structure of a vector space. With matrix addition and matrix multiplication, it has the structure of a ring. A system that has such a double structure is known as an *algebra*. Roughly, an algebra may be described as a ring that also

156

has a scalar multiplication defined for it, or a vector space that also has a binary operation of multiplication defined for it. The algebra we have just examined is only one of many possible algebras. In fact, by using definitions of addition, scalar multiplication, and matrix multiplication analogous to those given for 2 by 2 matrices, we can construct an algebra of 3 by 3 matrices, an algebra of 4 by 4 matrices, etc.

Rectangular Matrices

So far we have considered as matrices only square arrays of numbers. However, it is possible to extend the concept of a matrix to include rectangular arrays as well. If a rectangular array of numbers has two rows and five columns, for example, it is known as a 2 by 5 matrix. A vector space can be constructed out of all 2 by 5 matrices by defining matrix addition and scalar multiplication in the same way that we did for square matrices. In general, we can give a vector space structure in this way to the system of all rectangular matrices that have any fixed number of rows and any fixed number of columns. From this point of view, the vectors we first described in the last chapter turn out to be special cases of matrices. An ordered pair like (2, 3) is nothing but a 1 by 2 matrix. An ordered triple is a 1 by 3 matrix, and so on. It is also possible to have a 2 by 1 matrix that has two rows and one column, or a 3 by 1 matrix that has three rows and one column.

The definition of matrix multiplication can also be extended to rectangular matrices, with a special restriction that arises from the way in which matrix multiplication is carried out. To multiply two matrices, we have to multiply each of the rows of the first matrix by each of the columns in the second matrix. This is possible only if a row of the first matrix has as many components as a column does in the second matrix. This means that multiplication of matrices is possible only when the number of columns in the first matrix is equal to the number of rows in the second matrix. For example, we can multiply a 2 by 3 matrix times a 3 by 4 matrix, but we cannot multiply a 3 by 4 matrix times a 2 by 3 matrix.

Rectangular matrices give us a very powerful condensed language in which systems of several equations may sometimes be expressed as a single simple matrix equation. For example, consider these equations for a linear transformation that maps the ordered triples (x_1, x_2, x_3) into the ordered triples (y_1, y_2, y_3):

$$y_1 = a_1x_1 + a_2x_2 + a_3x_3$$

$$y_2 = b_1x_1 + b_2x_2 + b_3x_3$$

$$y_3 = c_1x_1 + c_2x_2 + c_3x_3$$

These three equations are equivalent to the single matrix equation:

$$\begin{vmatrix} y_1 \\ y_2 \\ y_3 \end{vmatrix} = \begin{vmatrix} a_1 & a_2 & a_3 \\ b_1 & b_2 & b_3 \\ c_1 & c_2 & c_3 \end{vmatrix} \cdot \begin{vmatrix} x_1 \\ x_2 \\ x_3 \end{vmatrix}$$

as you can verify by carrying out the matrix multiplication. If we introduce names for the matrices, as follows,

$$Y = \begin{vmatrix} y_1 \\ y_2 \\ y_3 \end{vmatrix} \qquad P = \begin{vmatrix} a_1 & a_2 & a_3 \\ b_1 & b_2 & b_3 \\ c_1 & c_2 & c_3 \end{vmatrix} \qquad X = \begin{vmatrix} x_1 \\ x_2 \\ x_3 \end{vmatrix},$$

then the equation takes the particularly simple form, $Y = PX$. Working with this single equation according to the rules of matrix algebra then takes the place of working with the three original equations.

Matrix algebra, one of the youngest branches of mathematics, is now one of the most widely used. Besides being an indispensable tool in higher mathematics, it is also employed in such diverse fields as psychology, chemistry, physics, economics, and electrical engineering.

158

DO IT YOURSELF

1. Find the sums $P + Q$ and $Q + P$, and the products PQ and QP of the following 2 by 2 matrices:

$$P = \begin{vmatrix} 2 & 1 \\ 4 & 3 \end{vmatrix} \qquad Q = \begin{vmatrix} 1 & 2 \\ 4 & 5 \end{vmatrix}$$

Compare your answers to verify that $P + Q = Q + P$, but PQ is not equal to QP.

2. a) Find the scalar product $2 \begin{vmatrix} a & b \\ c & d \end{vmatrix}$.

   b) Find the matrix product $\begin{vmatrix} 2 & 0 \\ 0 & 2 \end{vmatrix} \cdot \begin{vmatrix} a & b \\ c & d \end{vmatrix}$.

   Compare the results of both multiplications. Notice that the matrix $\begin{vmatrix} 2 & 0 \\ 0 & 2 \end{vmatrix}$, used with matrix multiplication, behaves like the scalar 2, used with scalar multiplication.

3. Let $P = \begin{vmatrix} 0 & 1 \\ 2 & 3 \end{vmatrix} \qquad Q = \begin{vmatrix} -1 & 2 \\ 4 & 3 \end{vmatrix} \qquad R = \begin{vmatrix} 2 & -1 \\ 6 & 5 \end{vmatrix}$

   a) Find $P(Q + R)$. That is, add Q and R, and then multiply by P from the left.
   b) Find $PQ + PR$. That is, find the products PQ and PR, and then add them.
   c) Compare the results of a) and b) to verify that the distributive law is obeyed.

4. Let $T = \begin{vmatrix} 0 & 1 & 0 \\ 0 & 0 & 1 \\ 0 & 0 & 0 \end{vmatrix}$

   a) Find $T^2 = TT$.
   b) Find $T^3 = T^2T$. What kind of element is T? (See page 156)

CHAPTER VIII

Arrows That Are Numbers

NOW WE return to unfinished business. In Chapter VI we had set out to accomplish a double purpose. We wanted to construct an extension of the real number system that would supply a number for every point in a plane, and would at the same time contain a number that satisfies the equation $x^2 = -1$. As the first step toward accomplishing this purpose we constructed a system in which each element is an ordered pair of real numbers, like (1, 4), or $(-\sqrt{2}, \frac{1}{2}\pi)$. We defined an operation of addition for these elements, and an operation we called scalar multiplication. With these two operations the system became an example of the type of structure we called a vector space.

In this vector space, we have an element for every point in the plane. However, this does not mean that we have already accomplished our purpose. Our goal was to find a *number system* that supplies an element for every point in the plane. The vector space we have constructed does not yet qualify as a number system. A structure is entitled to be called a number system only if it has two binary operations called addition and multiplication, such that each of these operations is associative and commutative, and multiplication is distributive with respect to addition. In the vector space whose elements are ordered pairs, we have an addition operation that is associative and commutative. We also have the operation called scalar multiplication, but it does not help the system qualify as a number system, because scalar multiplication is not a binary operation. In scalar multiplication, we multiply a vector by an element that is outside the system of vectors. In a multiplication that is a binary operation, we would have to multiply a vector by a vector, and get a product that is also a vector. So, to complete our construction, we now define a multiplication of this kind.

Ordered Pairs Become Numbers

We define the multiplication of ordered pairs by the following equation: $(a, b) \cdot (c, d) = (ac - bd, ad + bc)$. (In this equation, ac means $a \cdot c$, in accordance with the custom of sometimes omitting the multiplication sign in indicated products.) With this definition, for example, the product $(2, 3) \cdot (4, 1)$ would be equal to $(2 \cdot 4 - 3 \cdot 1, 2 \cdot 1 + 3 \cdot 4) = (5, 14)$. Now we show that this operation is commutative and associative, and is distributive with respect to addition.

To show that multiplication of ordered pairs is commutative, we compare $(a, b) \cdot (c, d)$ with $(c, d) \cdot (a, b)$.

$$(a, b) \cdot (c, d) = (ac - bd, ad + bc)$$
$$(c, d) \cdot (a, b) = (ca - db, cb + da).$$

But, in the real number system, $ac - bd = ca - db$, and $ad + bc = cb + da$. So the two products are the same, and the commutative law is obeyed.

To show that multiplication of ordered pairs is associative, we compare $[(a, b) \cdot (c, d)] \cdot (e, f)$ with $(a, b) \cdot [(c, d) \cdot (e, f)]$.

$$[(a, b) \cdot (c, d)] \cdot (e, f) = (ac - bd, ad + bc) \cdot (e, f)$$
$$= ([ac - bd]e - [ad + bc]f, [ac - bd]f + [ad + bc]e)$$
$$= (ace - bde - adf - bcf, acf - bdf + ade + bce).$$
$$(a, b) \cdot [(c, d) \cdot (e, f)] = (a, b) \cdot (ce - df, cf + de)$$
$$= (a[ce - df] - b[cf + de], a[cf + de] + b[ce - df])$$
$$= (ace - adf - bcf - bde, acf + ade + bce - bdf).$$

The first component in each of these products is the sum of four terms. Notice that they are the same four terms, merely written in a different order. Therefore these components are equal. Similarly, the second components are equal, and therefore the two products are equal. So multiplication of ordered pairs obeys the associative law.

To show that multiplication of ordered pairs is distributive with respect to addition, we compare $(a, b) \cdot [(c, d) + (e, f)]$ with $(a, b) \cdot (c, d) + (a, b) \cdot (e, f)$.

$$(a, b) \cdot [(c, d) + (e, f)] = (a, b) \cdot (c + e, d + f)$$
$$= (a[c + e] - b[d + f], a[d + f] + b[c + e])$$
$$= (ac + ae - bd - bf, ad + af + bc + be).$$

$$(a, b) \cdot (c, d) + (a, b) \cdot (e, f)$$
$$= (ac - bd, ad + bc) + (ae - bf, af + be)$$
$$= ([ac - bd] + [ae - bf], [ad + bc] + [af + be])$$
$$= (ac - bd + ae - bf, ad + bc + af + be).$$

The comparison shows that both expressions lead to the same result, and the distributive law is obeyed.

With the addition defined in Chapter VI, and with this new kind of multiplication, the system of ordered pairs of real numbers obeys the five laws that are characteristic of a number system. So now, at last, we have a number system that supplies a number for every point in a plane. We saw in Chapter VI that each ordered pair can be represented pictorially by an arrow, and the operations defined for ordered pairs may be interpreted as operations with the arrows. So we have, in effect, converted the system of arrows into a number system. We call it the system of *complex numbers*.

We have already observed, in Chapter VI, that the system of ordered pairs is an abelian group with respect to addition. Now that we have for this system a binary operation of multiplication that is associative and obeys the distributive law, the system meets the requirements for being a ring. But we already know that it is a vector space, equipped with a scalar multiplication. So the system of complex numbers has a double structure and therefore qualifies as an *algebra* in the sense of the definition given on page 156.

The Complex Number System Is a Field

To qualify as a field as well as a ring, the complex number system must meet the requirements of having a unity element, and having a reciprocal for every element except the zero element. We observe first that the complex number $(1, 0)$ is a unity element for the system, because when it multiplies any number in the system, it leaves that number unchanged:

$$(1, 0) \cdot (a, b) = (1 \cdot a - 0 \cdot b, 1 \cdot b + 0 \cdot a) = (a, b).$$

Now we shall produce a reciprocal for every complex number that is different from the zero element. The zero element in the complex number system is $(0, 0)$. So a complex number (a, b) is the zero element only if $a = 0$ and $b = 0$. If a complex number is different from the zero element, then a and b are not both zero. In that case, $a^2 + b^2$ is not zero, so that division by $a^2 + b^2$ is possible. So, if (a, b) is not the zero element, the symbols $\dfrac{a}{a^2 + b^2}$ and $-\dfrac{b}{a^2 + b^2}$ represent actual real numbers, and the ordered pair $\left(\dfrac{a}{a^2+b^2}, -\dfrac{b}{a^2+b^2}\right)$ is a complex number. We now show that it is the reciprocal of (a, b) by showing that their product is equal to the unity element:

$$(a, b) \cdot \left(\frac{a}{a^2 + b^2}, -\frac{b}{a^2 + b^2}\right)$$

$$= \left(a\left[\frac{a}{a^2+b^2}\right] - b\left[-\frac{b}{a^2+b^2}\right], \ a\left[-\frac{b}{a^2+b^2}\right] + b\left[\frac{a}{a^2+b^2}\right]\right)$$

$$= \left(\frac{a^2}{a^2 + b^2} + \frac{b^2}{a^2 + b^2}, -\frac{ab}{a^2 + b^2} + \frac{ab}{a^2 + b^2}\right)$$

$$= \left(\frac{a^2 + b^2}{a^2 + b^2}, 0\right) = (1, 0).$$

163

For example, the reciprocal of $(3, 4)$ is $(\frac{3}{25}, -\frac{4}{25})$.

This fact can be verified separately by multiplication:

$$(3, 4) \cdot (\tfrac{3}{25}, -\tfrac{4}{25}) = (3 \cdot [\tfrac{3}{25}] - 4[-\tfrac{4}{25}], 3[-\tfrac{4}{25}] + 4[\tfrac{3}{25}])$$

$$= (\tfrac{9}{25} + \tfrac{16}{25}, -\tfrac{12}{25} + \tfrac{12}{25}) = (1, 0)$$

We Still Have the Real Numbers

When we constructed the system of integers, we showed that there is a subset of the integers, the positive integers, that is isomorphic to the natural number system, and therefore can take its place for all practical purposes. In this sense, the system of integers includes the system of natural numbers, and is therefore an extension of the natural number system. In the same way we showed that the rational number system includes a subset isomorphic to the integers, and the real number system includes a subset isomorphic to the rational numbers. Now we show that the complex number system includes a subset isomorphic to the real numbers, and is therefore an extension of the real number system.

Before we display this subset, let us first introduce a new notation analogous to the i, j, k notation used for three dimensional vectors in Chapter VI. The complex number system is a two dimensional vector space, and all of its elements can be expressed in terms of the two unit vectors $(1, 0)$ and $(0, 1)$. We have already seen that $(1, 0)$ is the unity element of the system, so let us call it u, to remind us of that fact. We assign the name i to the vector $(0, 1)$. Then, the complex number $(a, b) = (a, 0) + (0, b) = a \cdot (1, 0) + b \cdot (0, 1) = au + bi$. These equalities follow from the rules for vector addition and scalar multiplication. Now we shall show that the real number system is isomorphic to the subset of the complex number system consisting of those ordered pairs in which the second component is 0. All the numbers in this subset have the special form $(a, 0) = a \cdot (1, 0) = au$. To prove the isomorphism we have to produce a one-to-one correspondence in which the image of a sum is the sum of the images, and the image of a product is the product of the images.

The one-to-one correspondence we use is the mapping $a \leftrightarrow au$. That is, we associate with each real number a the complex number that is equal to a times the unity element u. Under this mapping, the image of 1 is $1u$, the image of 5 is $5u$, the image of $\frac{1}{2}$ is $\frac{1}{2}u$, the image of $\sqrt{3}$ is $\sqrt{3}u$, the image of -2 is $-2u$. The image of 0 is $0u = 0(1, 0) = (0, 0) =$ the zero element of the complex number system. The image of $a + b$ is $(a + b)u$, and the image of ab is $(ab)u$.

Now let us compare the image of a sum with the sum of the images. The image of a is au. The image of b is bu. The sum of the images is $au + bu = a(1, 0) + b(1, 0) = (a, 0) + (b, 0) = (a + b, 0) = (a + b)(1, 0) = (a + b)u$. But this is precisely the image of the sum $a + b$ under the mapping. So the image of a sum is the sum of the images, and the mapping preserves addition.

Now let us compare the image of a product with the product of the images. The product of the images is $(au) \cdot (bu) = [a(1, 0)] \cdot [b(1, 0)] = (a, 0) \cdot (b, 0) = (ab - 0 \cdot 0, a \cdot 0 + b \cdot 0) = (ab, 0) = (ab)(1, 0) = (ab)u$. But this is precisely the image of the product ab. So the image of a product is the product of the images, and the mapping preserves multiplication. Therefore, in so far as the binary operations of addition and multiplication are concerned, the complex number au behaves just like the real number a, and, in particular, the unity element u behaves just like the real number 1. However, we have one more comparison to make, before we can agree that real numbers and complex numbers of the form au are interchangeable. The real number system does a special job in relation to the complex number system when it serves as the field of scalars for scalar multiplication. We have to check whether complex numbers of the form au can serve as scalars, too. To answer this question, we multiply any complex number (c, d) by the scalar a, using scalar multiplication, of course. Then we multiply the same complex number (c, d) by the complex image of a, namely au. Since both (c, d) and au

are complex numbers, this multiplication will be the binary operation defined for the complex number system. Then we compare the results.

Scalar multiplication: $a(c, d) = (ac, ad)$.

Complex number multiplication:

$$(au) \cdot (c, d) = [a(1, 0)] \cdot (c, d) = (a, 0) \cdot (c, d)$$
$$= (ac - 0 \cdot d, \, ad + 0 \cdot c) = (ac, ad).$$

The products are the same! Multiplication by the complex number au produces the same result as scalar multiplication by the real number a. So the complex numbers of the form au and the real numbers are completely equivalent, and the complex number system is an extension of the real number system. We can now dispense with the special symbol u, and replace it by 1, the symbol for the real number that it is equivalent to. Similarly, we write a for the complex number au. So now, the complex number (a, b), which we have written as $au + bi$, may be written as $a + bi$. The a is referred to as its real part and the bi is referred to as its *imaginary part*, and the complex number i is called the imaginary unit. In this notation, a real number is a complex number $a + bi$ whose imaginary part has $b = 0$.

The fact that scalar multiplication by the real number a is equivalent to multiplication by the complex number au (now also designated by a) makes it unnecessary to retain scalar multiplication as a separate operation for the algebra of complex numbers. Any time we need scalar multiplication, we merely think of it as the special case of the multiplication of complex numbers that arises when one of the multipliers happens to be a real number.

The Question Is Answered

One of our purposes in constructing the system of complex numbers was to have a system in which the equation

$x^2 = -1$ has a solution. We can now show that this purpose has been achieved. First let us be sure that we can recognize -1 in this system when we see it. The number -1, as an element in the complex number system, is equivalent to what we called $-1u$ before, which is $-1(1, 0)$, or $(-1, 0)$. It is in this form that we shall encounter it. The equation that we are trying to solve asks the question, "What number multiplied by itself gives -1 as the product?" We now show that the imaginary unit i provides the answer to the question.

$$i \cdot i = (0, 1) \cdot (0, 1) = (0 \cdot 0 - 1 \cdot 1, 0 \cdot 1 + 1 \cdot 0)$$
$$= (-1, 0) = -1.$$

Now that we have established the fact that $i^2 = i \cdot i = -1$, we can discard the cumbersome apparatus of ordered pairs, and work with complex numbers in a particularly easy way. We write them in the form $a + bi$, as we have already done, and we add them and multiply them according to the rules of elementary high school algebra, making use of the special rule that $i^2 = -1$. How addition and multiplication of complex numbers are carried out in this notation is shown in the following examples:

To add $(2 + 3i) + (-5 + 6i)$:

$$\begin{array}{r} 2 + 3i \\ -5 + 6i \\ \hline -3 + 9i \end{array}$$

To multiply $(2 + 3i)(-5 + 6i)$:

$$\begin{array}{r} 2 + 3i \\ -5 + 6i \\ \hline -10 - 15i \\ + 12i + 18i^2 \\ \hline -10 - 3i \ + 18(-1) \end{array}$$

$$= -28 - 3i$$

167

Bad Names for Good Numbers

Complex numbers were first introduced by the Italian mathematicians of the sixteenth century, who found, as we have, that they could not solve certain equations without them. However, mathematicians in those days were accustomed to think in terms of only one number system of positive and negative numbers. They considered the numbers in this system genuine, and therefore called them "real." The complex numbers clearly did not belong to the "real" number system, so, although they used them as a convenience, they considered them to be spurious, or unreal, and called them "imaginary." In fact, the great seventeenth century mathematician, René Descartes, was so doubtful of the reality of these numbers that he rejected them altogether. Today we realize that there is not only one number system. There are many number systems. All are equally genuine, although they differ from each other. Nevertheless we still use the old names, "real" numbers and "imaginary" numbers. So we must be careful not to be influenced by the old prejudices that are expressed in these names. When we use the term "imaginary numbers" now, we must bear in mind that it is a technical term, and should not be interpreted as a derogatory epithet casting doubt on the genuineness of the numbers.

Imaginary numbers are genuine numbers. We have demonstrated their existence by constructing them in the form of ordered pairs of real numbers. However, in order to dispel any lingering doubts that may remain about their genuineness, we now proceed to construct them by two other methods. After constructing complex numbers in three different ways, we ought to feel certain that they are genuine, though not "real."

Complex Numbers as Matrices

The second construction of the complex number system requires no new act of creation on our part. We find that the complex numbers are actually hidden in one of the struc-

168

tures we built up before. They form a subset of the algebra of 2 by 2 matrices defined in Chapter VII. In fact, the complex numbers are nothing else but the 2 by 2 matrices of the form $\begin{vmatrix} a & b \\ -b & a \end{vmatrix}$, in which the components in the upper left hand corner and the lower right hand corner are the same real number, and the other two components have the property that each is the negative of the other. Examples of this type of matrix are:

$$\begin{vmatrix} 2 & 3 \\ -3 & 2 \end{vmatrix} \quad \begin{vmatrix} -6 & -5 \\ 5 & -6 \end{vmatrix} \quad \begin{vmatrix} 1 & 0 \\ 0 & 1 \end{vmatrix} \quad \begin{vmatrix} 0 & 0 \\ 0 & 0 \end{vmatrix} \quad \begin{vmatrix} 0 & 1 \\ -1 & 0 \end{vmatrix}.$$

It may seem strange for this to be true, in view of the fact that multiplication of matrices is not commutative, while multiplication of complex numbers is commutative. However, while multiplication may not be commutative for a system as a whole, it may be commutative for some special subset in the system. In any case, we can easily prove that multiplication is commutative for the 2 by 2 matrices that have this special form. We compare

$$\begin{vmatrix} a & b \\ -b & a \end{vmatrix} \cdot \begin{vmatrix} c & d \\ -d & c \end{vmatrix} \quad \text{with} \quad \begin{vmatrix} c & d \\ -d & c \end{vmatrix} \cdot \begin{vmatrix} a & b \\ -b & a \end{vmatrix},$$

and show that the products are the same.

$$\begin{vmatrix} a & b \\ -b & a \end{vmatrix} \cdot \begin{vmatrix} c & d \\ -d & c \end{vmatrix} = \begin{vmatrix} a(c) + b(-d) & a(d) + b(c) \\ -b(c) + a(-d) & -b(d) + a(c) \end{vmatrix}$$

$$= \begin{vmatrix} ac - bd & ad + bc \\ -bc - ad & -bd + ac \end{vmatrix}.$$

$$\begin{vmatrix} c & d \\ -d & c \end{vmatrix} \cdot \begin{vmatrix} a & b \\ -b & a \end{vmatrix} = \begin{vmatrix} c(a) + d(-b) & c(b) + d(a) \\ -d(a) + c(-b) & -d(b) + c(a) \end{vmatrix}$$

$$= \begin{vmatrix} ac - bd & bc + ad \\ -ad - bc & -bd + ac \end{vmatrix}.$$

169

An examination of the two products, component by component, shows that they are the same.

Actually, it is not necessary to give this special proof that multiplication of these matrices is commutative. All we really have to do is show that the system of these special matrices is isomorphic with the complex number system we already have. Once we have established this fact, then it follows that the system of special matrices has all the properties that the complex number system has, including the commutativity of multiplication.

To prove that the two systems are isomorphic, we make use of the mapping $a + bi = (a, b) \longleftrightarrow \begin{vmatrix} a & b \\ -b & a \end{vmatrix}$.

Under this mapping, $(0, 0)$ is associated with $\begin{vmatrix} 0 & 0 \\ 0 & 0 \end{vmatrix}$, $(1, 0)$ is associated with $\begin{vmatrix} 1 & 0 \\ 0 & 1 \end{vmatrix}$, and $(0, 1)$ is associated with $\begin{vmatrix} 0 & 1 \\ -1 & 0 \end{vmatrix}$. This mapping is clearly a one-to-one correspondence. Now we show that it preserves addition and multiplication. The ordered pairs (a, b) and (c, d) have the sum $(a + c, b + d)$. Their images in the system of matrices are $\begin{vmatrix} a & b \\ -b & a \end{vmatrix}$ and $\begin{vmatrix} c & d \\ -d & c \end{vmatrix}$. These images have the matrix sum $\begin{vmatrix} a + c & b + d \\ -b - d & a + c \end{vmatrix}$, which is the image of the ordered pair $(a + c, b + d)$ under the mapping. So the sum of the images is the image of the sum.

The ordered pairs (a, b) and (c, d) have the product $(ac - bd, ad + bc)$. Their images, $\begin{vmatrix} a & b \\ -b & a \end{vmatrix}$ and $\begin{vmatrix} c & d \\ -d & c \end{vmatrix}$, have the matrix product $\begin{vmatrix} ac - bd & ad + bc \\ -bc - ad & -bd + ac \end{vmatrix}$, as shown on page 169. But this product is the image of the ordered pair $(ac - bd, ad + bc)$ under the mapping. So the product of the images is the image of the product. Therefore this system of special 2 by 2 matrices is isomorphic to the complex number system. It is nothing but the complex number system masquerading in a different style of dress. In this representation, the number 1 appears as $\begin{vmatrix} 1 & 0 \\ 0 & 1 \end{vmatrix}$.

The real numbers have the form $\begin{vmatrix} a & 0 \\ 0 & a \end{vmatrix}$. The numbers bi, whose real part is zero, have the form $\begin{vmatrix} 0 & b \\ -b & 0 \end{vmatrix}$. Consequently, the number i is $\begin{vmatrix} 0 & 1 \\ -1 & 0 \end{vmatrix}$, and the number -1 is $\begin{vmatrix} -1 & 0 \\ 0 & -1 \end{vmatrix}$.

We can verify directly by matrix multiplication that the number i in this form satisfies the equation $x^2 = -1$:

$$i^2 = \begin{vmatrix} 0 & 1 \\ -1 & 0 \end{vmatrix} \cdot \begin{vmatrix} 0 & 1 \\ -1 & 0 \end{vmatrix} = \begin{vmatrix} 0 \cdot 0 + 1(-1) & 0 \cdot 1 + 1 \cdot 0 \\ -1 \cdot 0 + 0(-1) & -1 \cdot 1 + 0 \cdot 0 \end{vmatrix}$$

$$= \begin{vmatrix} -1 & 0 \\ 0 & -1 \end{vmatrix} = -1.$$

Complex Numbers as Residue Classes

The third method of constructing the complex number system follows a procedure we have already used before. In Chapter III we divided the system of integers into residue classes modulo 3, by putting together into the same class all integers that have the same remainder when we divide them by 3. We defined operations of addition and multiplication for these residue classes. Then we found that, with these operations, the residue classes formed a number system. In Chapter IV we found out that the system of residue classes modulo 3 is also a field. We are now

171

going to go through these steps in the same order. First, we shall construct a ring that will play the same part here that the ring of integers did in Chapter III. Then we shall divide it into residue classes, by putting into the same class all members of the ring that have the same remainder when we divide by a particular member of the ring specially chosen for our purpose. Then, with addition and multiplication of residue classes defined as it was in Chapter III we shall find that the system of residue classes is a number system, and a field. Finally, we shall show that this number system is nothing but the complex number system in disguise.

The elements that we use for the ring that we start with are the polynomials whose terms are powers of x with coefficients that are real numbers. In this system, each separate real number, like $\frac{1}{2}$, or 2, or $\sqrt{3}$, is a polynomial of zero degree. Then there are polynomials of the first degree, like $2x + 5$, and $\sqrt{3}x - 7$. There are polynomials of the second degree, like $x^2 - 1$, $x^2 + 1$, and polynomials of higher degree like $2x^3 - 5x^2 + 6x + 7$, $x^5 - 4x + 1$, etc. On page 134, we saw that this system of polynomials is a vector space. The addition in this vector space is the ordinary addition of polynomials we learned in high school algebra. The polynomials form an abelian group with respect to this operation of addition. The zero element for this operation is the real number 0, considered as a polynomial of no degree. Now we introduce an operation of multiplication of polynomials by using the rules of multiplication taught in elementary high school algebra. For example, we obtain the product $(2x + 1)(3x - 5)$ in this way:

$$
\begin{array}{r}
3x - 5 \\
2x + 1 \\
\hline
6x^2 - 10x \\
+ \ 3x - 5 \\
\hline
6x^2 - \ 7x - 5
\end{array}
$$

This operation of multiplication of polynomials is associative and commutative, and it is distributive with respect to

172

addition. So the system of polynomials has the structure of a ring. The unity element for multiplication of polynomials is the real number 1 considered as a polynomial of zero degree.

The next step we take is influenced by the purpose we are trying to accomplish. Our goal, you will recall, is to construct a number system in which the equation $x^2 + 1 = 0$ has a solution. The polynomial that appears in this equation plays a special part in the next step of our construction. We use it as a divisor, and divide it into every other polynomial in the system. Where the division comes out even, we get a quotient, and a remainder equal to zero. Where the division does not come out even, the remainder is different from zero. For example, when we divide $x^4 + 3x^2 + 2$ by $x^2 + 1$, the quotient is $x^2 + 2$, and the remainder is 0. When we divide $x^2 + 1$ by $x^2 + 1$, the quotient is 1, and the remainder is 0. When we divide 0 by $x^2 + 1$, the quotient is 0, and the remainder is 0. When we divide $x^2 + 2$ by $x^2 + 1$, the quotient is 1 and the remainder is 1. When we divide x by $x^2 + 1$, the quotient is 0, and the remainder is x. When we divide $x^2 + 3x + 5$ by $x^2 + 1$, the quotient is 1, and the remainder is $3x + 4$.

In arithmetic, when we divide one integer by another, the remainder is always smaller than the divisor. There is an analogous rule for the division of polynomials. When we divide one polynomial by another, the remainder is always a polynomial of lower degree than the divisor. This is so because, as long as the remainder has the same degree as the divisor, or a higher degree, the division can be carried out for at least one more step. This is seen in the succession of steps for dividing $2x^3 - 3x^2 + 4x - 1$ by $x^2 + 1$:

$$
\begin{array}{r}
2x - 3 \\
x^2 + 1 \overline{\smash{\big)}\ 2x^3 - 3x^2 + 4x - 1} \\
\underline{2x^3 + 2x } \\
-3x^2 + 2x - 1 \\
\underline{-3x^2 - 3} \\
2x + 2
\end{array}
$$

The remainder in this case is $2x + 2$. Since the divisor $x^2 + 1$ is of the second degree, all remainders we get will be of the first degree or the zero degree. They will therefore be in the form $a + bx$, where a and b are real numbers. The remainder is of zero degree in the cases where b happens to be 0.

Now we sort all the polynomials in the ring into residue classes, by putting together in the same class all polynomials that have the same remainder when they are divided by $x^2 + 1$. We shall designate each class by a symbol of the form C_P, where P is a polynomial that belongs to the class. Thus each class has many names, and we recognize that two names stand for the same class when we see that the polynomials written as subscripts have the same remainder when we divide by $x^2 + 1$. For example, C_0, $C_{x^2 + 1}$, and $C_{x^4 + 3x^2 + 2}$ all stand for the same class, because the polynomials 0, $x^2 + 1$, and $x^4 + 3x^2 + 2$ all have the remainder 0 when they are divided by $x^2 + 1$. The polynomial x belongs to the class C_x. The polynomial a, where a is a real number, belongs to the class C_a. Since different real numbers have different remainders when they are divided by $x^2 + 1$ (each is its own remainder), no two real numbers belong to the same class.

We define operations of addition and multiplication of residue classes in the same way that we did for residue classes modulo 3 in Chapter III. To add two residue classes, pick a polynomial from each class, and add them. Then identify the class to which the sum of the polynomials belongs. That class will be the sum of the two classes. In the notation we are using, a member of each class is always put on display as a subscript in the name of the class. So we can add two classes by merely adding their subscripts. For example, $C_2 + C_3 = C_5$. $C_{2x} + C_7 = C_{2x + 7}$.

To multiply two residue classes, we multiply a polynomial in one class by a polynomial in the other, and find the class that the product belongs to. Since a member of each class is put on display as a subscript in the name of the class, we can multiply two classes by merely multiplying their subscripts.

With these definitions of addition and multiplication, the system of residue classes has the structure of a ring and a number system. This follows from the fact that addition and multiplication in the system are commutative and associative, and multiplication is distributive with respect to addition. We can verify the commutativity of addition very easily. $C_P + C_Q = C_{P+Q}$, and $C_Q + C_P = C_{Q+P}$. But addition of polynomials is commutative, so $P + Q = Q + P$, and therefore $C_{P+Q} = C_{Q+P}$. The other properties are established by a similar argument. The zero element in the ring is C_0, because if C_P is the class of any polynomial P, $C_0 + C_P = C_{0+P} = C_P$.

Within this number system, there is a subset that is isomorphic to the real number system. This subset consists of all classes of the form C_a, where a is a real number (that is, a polynomial of zero degree). To prove that it is isomorphic to the real number system, we have to produce a one-to-one correspondence that preserves the operations of addition and multiplication. The mapping we use for this purpose is $a \leftrightarrow C_a$. The mapping is a one-to-one correspondence, because no two different real numbers belong to the same class. Under this mapping, if a and b are two real numbers, their images are C_a and C_b. The sum of the images is $C_a + C_b = C_{a+b}$, which is the image of the sum. The product of the images is $C_a \cdot C_b = C_{ab}$, which is the image of the product. Therefore the set of classes of the form C_a, where a is a real number, is isomorphic to the real number system. Since isomorphic systems are the same for all practical purposes, we can use the symbols of one system to represent the other. So now, instead of writing C_a for the class to which a real number a belongs, we shall simply write a. Thus 0 will stand for C_0, 1 will stand for C_1, and -1 will stand for C_{-1}.

Now that we have found the real numbers within our new system, we know that it is an extension of the real number system. Next we observe that it contains an element that is a solution to the equation $x^2 + 1 = 0$. To show that this is so, we must produce a class C_P which has the property that $(C_P) \cdot (C_P) + 1 = 0$. The class that has this property is the class C_x. In fact, $C_x \cdot C_x + 1 = C_x \cdot C_x + C_1 = C_{x^2} + C_1 = C_{x^2 + 1} = C_0 = 0$. Notice that we made use of the fact that when $x^2 + 1$ is divided by $x^2 + 1$, the remainder is 0, so that $C_{x^2 + 1} = C_0$.

The class C_x therefore has the same property as the complex number we called i before. In fact, since x^2 has the remainder -1 when we divide it by $x^2 + 1$, $C_x \cdot C_x = C_{x^2} = C_{-1} = -1$. Let us therefore use the symbol i to stand for C_x, since the rule $i^2 = -1$ holds for C_x as well.

Now only one more step remains to show that this system of residue classes is essentially the same as the complex number system we built up before. We show that it is isomorphic to the complex number system. First let us remind ourselves that every class in the system can be represented by the remainder that the members of the class have in common. Secondly, we recall that all remainders, when we divide by $x^2 + 1$, are first degree polynomials of the form $a + bx$ where a and b are real numbers. So every member of our new class of numbers can be represented in the form $C_{a + bx}$. Now, using the rules for addition and multiplication of residue classes, we see that $C_{a + bx}$ can be written as $C_a + C_b \cdot C_x$. We have already agreed to write a instead of C_a, and b instead of C_b, because classes of this special form behave like real numbers. We have also agreed to write i for C_x, because the rule that $i^2 = -1$ correctly describes the behavior of this class. So we can write $C_a + C_b \cdot C_x$ in the form $a + bi$, with the understanding that a and b behave like real numbers and i has the property $i^2 = -1$. When we write it this way we see that the residue class $C_{a + bx}$ is nothing but the complex number $a + bi$ in disguise. The system of residue classes modulo $(x^2 + 1)$ is therefore the field of complex numbers. This completes the third construction of the complex number system.

We have now seen the system of complex numbers in

176

three forms of dress. We have seen it as a system of ordered pairs, as a system of two by two matrices, and as a system of residue classes in a ring of polynomials. In each of these systems, an individual complex number has a different appearance. But the structure of the three systems, in so far as their addition and multiplication tables are concerned, is the same. So we recognize them as merely different representations of one and the same number system, whose elements are usually represented in the convenient form $a + bi$.

No More Extensions Needed

We have expanded our number system four times. Each expansion to a more extensive system was made necessary by the fact that a certain type of equation could not be solved in the less extensive system. In the natural number system, we could not solve an equation like $x + 5 = 3$. So we constructed the system of integers, where all equations of the form $x + b = a$ have a solution. In the system of integers, we could not solve an equation like $2x = 3$. So we constructed the system of rational numbers, in which all equations of the form $ax = b$ have a solution, as long as a is not equal to 0. At this stage, we found that we could always solve equations of the first degree, whose general form is $ax + b = 0$. But we could not say the same for equations of the second degree. To be able to solve the equation $x^2 - 2 = 0$, we had to construct the real number system. To be able to solve the equation $x^2 + 1 = 0$, we had to construct the complex number system.

Now it is worth asking what equations we can solve in the complex number system. So far we have examined only equations of the first and second degree. If we try other algebraic equations of higher degree, will we find any that cannot be solved in the complex number system? Will it be necessary to expand the number system again and again, as we try more and more complicated algebraic equations? If you have had visions of an endless chain of extensions of the number system, you can dismiss them at once. As far as algebraic equations are concerned, we have reached the end of the road. The complex number system not only gives us a solution to the equation $x^2 + 1 = 0$. It gives us a solution for *every other algebraic equation* as well. To be more specific, it is known that every algebraic equation of the form

$$a_n x^n + a_{n-1} x^{n-1} \cdots a_1 x + a_0 = 0,$$

whose coefficients are complex numbers, has a solution in the complex number system. In fact it has as many solutions as the degree of the equation indicates. A first degree equation has one solution, a second degree equation has two solutions, a third degree equation has three solutions, and so on. The fact that algebraic equations can always be solved within the complex number system is known as the Fundamental Theorem of Algebra. It was first proved by the great German mathematician, Carl Friedrich Gauss (1777-1855).

The Old in the New

We have accomplished the purpose we aimed for at the beginning of the book. We have seen how, through successive extensions of the number system, mathematicians have eliminated its defects while losing none of its virtues. We have been introduced to a variety of mathematical structures, like groups, rings, fields, vector spaces, and topological spaces, that are being explored vigorously in mathematics today. We have found that, although their names are new, and at first sound unfamiliar, they are closely related to such familiar things as addition and multiplication of numbers, and collections of points on a line. Although the world of modern mathematics is a new world in many ways, it has never lost contact with the old world of number and space from which it has grown.

DO IT YOURSELF

1. Use the definition of multiplication of ordered pairs (see page 161) to find the following products:

$(2, 3) \cdot (4, 1)$ $(2, 3) \cdot (2, -3)$ $(2, 0) \cdot (0, 3)$

2. Write each of these ordered pairs in the form $a + bi$, making use of the convention that 1 stands for $(1, 0)$, and i stands for $(0, 1)$:

   $(2, 3)$ $(2, -3)$ $(3, 0)$ $(0, 2)$

3. Verify by multiplication that $\frac{1}{2} - \frac{1}{2}i$ is the reciprocal of $1 + i$. (Remember that $i^2 = -1$)

4. Let 1 stand for the two by two matrix $\begin{vmatrix} 1 & 0 \\ 0 & 1 \end{vmatrix}$, and let

   i stand for the two by two matrix $\begin{vmatrix} 0 & 1 \\ -1 & 0 \end{vmatrix}$.

   Write the two by two matrices that represent $2 + 3i$ and $2 - 3i$. Verify by matrix multiplication that $(2 + 3i) \cdot$

   $(2 - 3i) = 13 = \begin{vmatrix} 13 & 0 \\ 0 & 13 \end{vmatrix}$.

5. Use the rules for addition and multiplication of residue classes modulo $(x^2 + 1)$ to verify the following sums or products:

   $C_{2x^2+1} + C_1 = C_0$. $C_x \cdot C_{2x} = C_{-2}$.
   $C_{x+1} \cdot C_{x+2} = C_{3x+1}$. $C_{x^2} + C_3 = C_2$.

Bibliography

For readers who wish to learn more about the subjects discussed in this book:

Elements of Algebra, by Howard Levi
    Chelsea Publishing Co., New York
Higher Algebra for the Undergraduate, by Marie J. Weiss
    John Wiley & Sons, New York
A Survey of Modern Algebra, by Garrett Birkhoff & Saunders MacLane, The Macmillian Company, New York

Summary of Basic Definitions

Zero element: A is a zero element for addition if $A + X = X + A = X$, for every X.

Unity element: U is a unity element for multiplication if $U \cdot X = X \cdot U = X$, for every X.

Identity element: E is an identity element for the operation $*$ if $E * X = X * E = X$, for every X.

Negative: A is the negative of B if $A + B = B + A = 0$.

Reciprocal: A is the reciprocal of B if $A \cdot B = B \cdot A = 1$.

Inverse: A is the inverse of B with respect to the operation $*$ whose identity element is E, if $A * B = B * A = E$.

Commutative: Addition is commutative if $x + y = y + x$. Multiplication is commutative if $x \cdot y = y \cdot x$.

Associative: Addition is associative if $(x + y) + z = x + (y + z)$. Multiplication is associative if $(x \cdot y) \cdot z = x \cdot (y \cdot z)$.

Distributive: Multiplication is distributive with respect to addition if $x \cdot (y + z) = x \cdot y + x \cdot z$.

Number system: A set of elements is a number system if it has two binary operations called addition and multiplication, each of which is commutative and associative, and if multiplication is distributive with respect to addition.

Group: A system is called a group if it has a binary operation that is associative, has an identity element for the operation, and has an inverse for every element. If the operation is commutative, the group is called abelian.

183

Ring: A system is called a ring if it has two associative binary operations called addition and multiplication, is an abelian group with respect to addition, and if the multiplication is distributive with respect to addition.

Field: A ring is called a field if it has a unity element for multiplication and contains a reciprocal for every element except 0.

Topological Space: A system of elements is called a topological space if a collection of its subsets is singled out to be called "open sets," and the collection has these properties: 1) The whole space and the empty set belong to the collection. 2) The union of any number of sets in the collection is also in the collection. 3) The intersection of any two sets in the collection is also in the collection.

Vector Space: A system is a vector space if it is an abelian group with respect to addition, is subject to a scalar multiplication by elements from an associated field of scalars, and if the scalar multiplication obeys these laws:

$$r \cdot (\vec{x} + \vec{y}) = r \cdot \vec{x} + r \cdot \vec{y}.$$

$$(r + s) \cdot \vec{x} = r \cdot \vec{x} + s \cdot \vec{x}$$

$$r \cdot (s \cdot \vec{x}) = (r \cdot s) \cdot \vec{x}$$

$$1 \cdot \vec{x} = \vec{x}.$$

Algebra: A system is an algebra if it is provided with binary operations of addition and multiplication, and a scalar multiplication, that make it both a vector space and a ring.

Geometry: A geometry is a study which identifies those figures in a space which are equivalent to each other under a group of transformations, and determines what properties equivalent figures have in common.

184

Index

185